A Symphony for Shelbie

Also by Carl Vigeland

Great Good Fortune (1986)

In Concert (1989)

Stalking the Shark (1996)

Jazz in the Bittersweet Blues of Life (with Wynton
  Marsalis; 2001)

Letters to a Young Golfer (with Bob Duval; 2002)

The Mostly Mozart Guide to Mozart (2009)

The Breathless Present (2011)

Jonathan Sternberg (2013)

The Great Romance (2014)

Dear President Trump (2019)

Carl Vigeland

A SYMPHONY
FOR SHELBIE

Combray House

ISBN 978-0-578-51906-7

for Jackie

~

This music crept by me upon the waters,
Allaying both their fury and my passion
With its sweet air. Thence I have followed it,
Or it hath drawn me rather. But 'tis gone.
No, it begins again.

Shakespeare

Contents

I: *Living With Cancer*

Listening on an early August morning —
warm, fragrant, a little muggy—as if for a lost angel's call, I'd taken the first seat I could find in the
front row of the Tanglewood Shed, the so-called
summer home of the Boston Symphony Orchestra
in the Berkshires of western Massachusetts. With
its dirt floor and a perimeter, except for the stage,
open to the outdoors, the Shed often felt to me
more like a huge tent, as if it were the big top in a
large circus. Had the exposed ceiling girders been
rigged with swings and wires for an aerial act, little else would be needed to complete the image, for
the great circus attraction to me has always been a
sense of magical transformation.

Having once heard the morning's French soloist, Jean-Yves Thibaudet, perform all of Ravel's

music for solo piano, I was expecting something beautiful, though I did not know the piece, a piano concerto by Saint Saens. Monsieur Thibaudet came out wearing designer jeans, a shirt or jacket a little Nehru-ish I think but can't recall for certain, and sky-blue patent leather loafers with no socks. Not that the shoes had anything to do with his phenomenal talent, but they did I thought convey a hint of the ebullient personality of a musician who, when he started to play, immediately took me to a place within myself I once knew and long departed people I still loved. Transfixed, I had a powerful sense of *knowing* that gnawed at my insides like the undertow of this vast ocean of sound, an aural truth that the circumstance of this orchestra and pianist seemed to be reminding me. If transcendence were real, it was getting late in my life to affirm it.

A Symphony for Shelbie

For as long ago as I can remember, I have taken the long road home, many times losing my way and then wondering afterwards why I made things so difficult for myself and, often as not, my friends and family. Afraid that all my talk of music was just talk, that everyone else understood some-thing about life I did not, or maybe that I under-stood something that no one else cared about, soon after that Tanglewood rehearsal I began to write a ghost story about loss called *Night Music*. Inspired initially by a friendship that had initiated mysteri-ously and ended ambiguously, the first draft came quickly into being. Over the next two years, I re-vised and reshaped both the form and the content of imagined scenes set off-season at the very place I heard that pianist. Narrated in the third person, the story, like life, kept evolving, but I could never figure out the ending. Then, during this same time, I met a doctor and some of her young patients, and

Vigeland

I began to wonder if ending were even the right term.

We live in an age where closure is a cliché, even as we celebrate "more"—bigger houses, greater incomes, faster cars—and assume the solution to any problem is to overwhelm it. "It became necessary to destroy the town to save it," a United States military officer famously said of a bombing campaign during the Vietnam War. We treat illness with an enormous barrage of expensive testing, care, and drugs. We bombard infection with antibiotics, while the very language of traditional cancer care, its mantra, still in the vast majority of cases speaks of killing it. Yet, bacteria become resistant to antibiotics. And for countless cancer patients undergoing the maximum tolerated dose of chemotherapy, the usual result is hair loss, nausea, and sleeplessness. Far too often, the cancer eventually returns, to be followed by a newer, stronger regimen of chemo. What if there were an alternative and doctors tried to do more with less, like a golfer facing a delicate chip or that pianist whose most exquisite moments came during quiet passages requiring the lightest touch?

Years ago, Wynton Marsalis, with whom I was collaborating on a book, told me I would have been killed and buried in a concrete coffin in the bayou, if a long piece about the murderer of a Mississippi civil rights martyr I'd written had been published by the magazine that had commissioned it. Instead, after a date was finally set for the murderer's retrial, when the magazine had originally planned to run the piece, there wasn't enough lead time for the magazine, or so they said.

Forgetting my disappointment, and discounting the hyperbole in Wynton's post-mortem, I replied that I'd already avoided the possibility of

Vigeland

death while reporting the story, when on a hot summer afternoon I'd driven by myself to a small town in southern Mississippi—even now, I'm afraid to name it—looking for an accomplice of the murderer and former KKK member, astonishingly a lawyer after serving jail time for another crime. As I'd waited in the man's outer office for him to finish a consultation, I'd had a premonition that I shouldn't have come alone and I left. All the way back to my motel, I could see in the rear view mirror the narrowing distance between me and an old pickup truck I'd noticed parked outside the lawyer's office as I'd departed.

On another hot Mississippi day I encountered a different lawyer, who seemed in some ways to be in charge of the community where he'd grown up and early in his career worked for the local district attorney—he'd actually helped prosecute the murderer's first trail, long before— and who among other things became a wealthy cotton farmer. Over bourbon in his downtown office—I wasn't asked what I'd like to drink; it was simply given to me—I confessed that I'd never seen an actual cotton plant. He invited me to visit his ranch or farm, don't remember what he called it, but upon my appearance at the appointed time the next day he ended up sending a crony in his place.

After we'd driven by what must once have been a plantation, where we parked and got out of the car to view acres of cotton that stretched from the road to the horizon, this man insisted on showing me a housing development. He was creating it with the help, he boasted, of some clever rezoning he'd managed to get through, which apparently green-lighted construction of basic services (water, sewer, and so on), without which the project would never have materialized. Then we stopped for a tour of his palatial new home. I still get the

Vigeland

creeps when I remember the feeling of unease that came over me as he led me upstairs to the master bedroom with his and her bathrooms and the pounding in my heart as he warned me about bringing up the past in what he told me was a newly "harmonious" present.

The deep sense of injustice and sadness I felt in Mississippi, coupled with fear—of the unknown, of evil—and the inscrutability of fate, of the universe, came back to me again as I attended the funeral for 17-year-old Shelbie Murphy, who died of cancer, in a Lowell, Massachusetts church just before Christmas in 2014. In my own life, it was as if at that moment everything I had experienced that I did not understand—the reason for a close relative's shock therapy, the mysterious source of what I eventually came to think of as another's PTSD, the tragic car accident that killed one of my high school classmates a few months before graduation—came back to me in ever growing multiplicity even as, simultaneously, I felt guilty for thinking about myself.

For four years, Shelbie had suffered from a rare form of bone cancer called Ewing's Sarcoma, which had manifested—presented, in medical jargon—in her pelvis and upon its diagnosis when she was 13 was already at stage four. Through long periods of many different medical procedures, including a bone marrow transplant, she had not only managed to return to school, where she studied art and design, but also to travel, going with her mother Jackie to the Bahamas, where during a magical afternoon she swam with the dolphins. On another occasion, she attended a Taylor Swift concert and afterwards met the popular singer. Less than a year before her death, after further therapy at Floating Hospital, she cheered for her favorite team, the Boston Bruins, at a hockey game at TD

Vigeland

Garden, where she sat near the ice and wore a Bruins jersey. And then, soon afterwards, knowing there was a risk to her bone structure, she chose anyway to attend a prom.

The church was packed for a ceremony that included communion. Shelbie's closed casket was placed by the pallbearers in front of the nave. A priest officiated, an organist and singer provided music, and one of Shelbie's aunts spoke with great emotion near the end, the rest of her family sitting in the front pews, her mother and father next to one another, and next to them her grandparents.

As I sat there, surrounded by hundreds of Shelbie's family members and friends, so many of them young, I remembered amidst the countless times I have been in a church—among other things, my father was a church musician— another moment in Mississippi, a candlelight service that was held on behalf of the surviving family of the man who had been murdered back in the 1960s.

The church was located next to the cemetery where the martyr was buried. Just before the service was to start, it began to rain, so the congregation had to move inside. A daughter named Bettie, who had been burned during the attack on her father, sat in the front pew, next to her mother, Ellie Jewel. The minister leading the service had asked for a family member to read one of the scriptures, and Bettie had volunteered. When it was time to do so she read from Saint Matthew, in a voice that was so gracefully inflected she might have been singing:

"Blessed are they which are persecuted for righteousness' sake: for theirs is the kingdom of heaven."

Vigeland

Then she took her seat next to her mother, and the Mount Carmel Baptist Church Inspirational Choir sang.

"Oh, freedom," the voices sang. "Before I be a slave, I'll be buried in my grave."

After the anthem, everyone joined in singing Amazing Grace. Then the pastor prayed aloud.

"What's been done in the dark will be brought to light," he said. And some in the congregation responded aloud, saying "Amen," or "That's right."

Speaking in a booming voice, he concluded, "If justice doesn't get you here, it will get you there."

Upset by the memories that had been stirred yet again, Ellie Jewell kept her eyes closed. Tears formed in the corners of her eyes and she let them come. Her head bowed in prayer, she wept. Finally, she stood and walked outside to greet people, to speak one at a time with each of those who had come to see her.

After the funeral service in Lowell, an older woman sitting behind me tapped me on the shoulder.

"I'm sorry to disturb you," she said. "But I noticed you were sitting alone. Are you perhaps Shelbie's doctor?"

That was certainly a first for me. The woman introduced herself and her husband, who was standing by her side and, if I followed correctly, worked with Shelbie's father, or maybe owned the business where her father worked. I did not catch his name, and we soon shook hands and walked outside. I looked in vain for Shelbie's oncologist, Dr. Giannoula Lakka Klement, with whom I'd had dinner less than a week before, and whom I learned later had been the only doctor on service

Vigeland

that day at her hospital and so, therefore, could not leave work. Nor did I see one of Shelbie's primary care nurses, Laura Eagles, with whom that final autumn she had talked often about her impending death.

"What do you think heaven is like?" Shelbie had asked Laura, during her last extended stay at the hospital. "I am so sorry for my parents that I have to go there before they do."

I had first heard Shelbie's name soon after meeting Dr. Klement—Giannoula, as she insisted she be addressed—over brunch more than a year before. We'd been introduced by one of the people who worked in her research lab, a young Russian-American mathematician named Irina Kareva who wrote equations that explained models of the revolutionary cancer therapies she told me Giannoula was practicing. Irina had entered my life by complete chance a few months before my meeting Giannoula. On a lovely July afternoon in Great Barrington, not far from Tanglewood, I was talking with a new friend, Lee Elman, on the patio of his home when he spotted a stranger hiking across his property.

As if by the very kind of seemingly inexplicable sequence of events that so often in the world and in our individual lives pass for cause and effect, my life was about to continue a change that I had yet to consciously trace back to the Tanglewood rehearsal, nor, of course, could I envision what grace might come.

I'd encountered Lee late the previous summer, a few weeks after attending the rehearsal with the French pianist. Beginning *Night Music*, I was checking some Berkshires geography before attending another Tanglewood event. Shunning

Vigeland

the main road, I'd driven from West Stockbridge through the nearby hamlet of Alford, looking first for an old inn that in my father's telling was the scene during his heyday of great parties, and then tracing the route of the Green River to a skinny dipping spot an old friend of my father's first told me about. My meanderings led me eventually to a hilltop park on the outskirts of trendy Great Barrington, once an outback and now a thriving center of chic restaurants and weekend retreats. I left my car and walked downhill by a lovely, fragrant meadow and then through some sun-dappled woods along a dirt road that ended at the river.

No naked people in the water that day, but the sound of the river running over rocks reminded me of a summer long past. I imagined I could hear my father's voice echoing over the gurgles and ripples of a white-foamed shallow pool in which he was standing, the water waist high, as he

A Symphony for Shelbie

carried on an animated conversation with one of my college classmates—this must have been 40 years ago, I calculated, when one of my father's old girlfriends had given our family her Great Barrington house for an entire summer while she and her dentist husband traveled. "Who knows a family as lucky as ours?" my father would say at such moments, and it was impossible as he spoke to know if this thought were a belief or a wish.

As I made my way back up to my car, I knew where I wanted to go next. With directions starting on Main Street, a block past the Castle Street corner that led to the historic Mahaiwe Theater, near the town's train station, long out of service, I took the next right and drove uphill by Fairview Hospital. Through a neighborhood of tidy middle class homes, I continued before turning at the last left onto Berkshire Heights, which brought me soon to an enormous strand of very tall, second-growth

Vigeland

pine trees. The street ended there, but I kept going, just as I knew my father would have, past a sign that said, in small letters, *Private,* and then in larger script, Aston Magna.

Along a winding, dirt and gravel driveway, framed by thousands of more trees, I drove by another sign on my left that said, Stable, and soon thereafter, on my right, a large, log-framed lodge. Finally, I came to a sudden airiness and brightness that presaged a break in the forest. The road now made a hairpin turn as I reached an open place that in one direction revealed an expansive view of the southern Berkshires in what seemed their inviting, soothing entirety and in the other, across a long lawn, a legendary house, once the domain of a famous American violinist for whom my father, for a brief period in his early adulthood—this would have been just before the Second World War—was his occasional rehearsal pianist. The view from that patio stretched out for miles over an enormous horizon, at the distant center of which was the mountaintop where, 30 years before, we had scattered my father's ashes.

It was there, nearly a year later, that I was talking with Lee in connection with a short book I'd started about Aston Magna—which had been Lee's weekend retreat since 1971—when in the distance we saw someone who, technically speaking, was trespassing that day, just as I had the summer before.

"It's okay!" Lee shouted.

Startled, the person stopped and turned around, and Lee, standing, repeated his welcome, adding a request that she come and say hello... which she did. Her name was Irina Kareva, and she told us she was staying with friends in Great Barrington for the several days because she was

Vigeland

singing on Saturday night as a member of the chorus in a BSO performance of Verdi's Requiem.

A polyglot, as I would learn, who in addition to her singing was a talented tango dancer, Irina had studied mathematics and music at the University of Maryland, College Park, and earned a
Ph.D. in applied mathematics at Arizona State
University in Tempe. She originally came from
Russia to the United States with her family (both
of her parents were also mathematicians) in 2000.
Now, she continued, she was a post-doc in Boston,
where she was doing mathematical modeling of
cancer therapies. What could the two have in common?

Though it did not occur to me right then, this
fateful meeting with Irina would eventually strike
me as symbolic of the very mysteries her equations
sought to describe: why person X with genome Y

developed cancer Z, while someone else whose circumstances might seem more predisposed to the same cancer never got sick, and how in the case of person X s/he should be treated.

I thought Irina would make a good subject for a magazine piece by a physician-writer I knew of through a close college friend who had been a patient. But I soon decided to try myself, swayed by her personality and challenged to rediscover my forgotten adolescent love of mathematics. In one of our many exchanges, she explained what she did in her mathematics by comparing it to biology, which, she told me, "is still largely a descriptive science, focusing on describing what things are. Mathematical models," she continued, "describe what things do. So, when used correctly, mathematical modeling can be an extremely powerful tool to assess whether the understanding of the biological process is correct.

Vigeland

"When I would come to my dad while I was in grad school and describe some cool process that I thought could be modeled, he would say, 'That is all very nice, but show me your equations. Then we'll talk.' Because mathematics allows no hand-waving."

While we spoke as well about music, Russia, her family, literature, and movies, always, as if the subject were threaded within her intense, energetic being, cancer would come up in the conversation. In both her life and her work, all these things seemed inter-related: everything connected, even if or especially if the connections were not always readily apparent. In fact, the word system was a constant in her vocabulary. Invariably as well in our conversations, Irina would at some point mention the "amazing" G.— that was what many who knew her apparently called Dr. Klement—and the radical approach to cancer therapy she was advocating and that Irina was modeling.

I vividly remember the moment that, as it turned out, all these meetings were leading to. Like the serendipity of my introduction to Irina, there was in the reaction I instantaneously felt upon sitting down for brunch with Giannoula a certainty of recognition that I would come to understand as characteristic of doctors and scientists when, within the miasma of false leads and shattered assumptions, they suddenly *see* or, as in my own case, *hear*.

"We have all these expertises, all this information," Giannoula told me when we finally met at a diner to which she'd biked, without a helmet, from her Fenway condo in Boston's Back Bay. "I even have my genome here," she continued, as she held up her iPhone. "It's like what has happened

with the stars that have been mapped, each identified with a name...but no one knows what the gal-
axy is called."

If I were wary about the prospect of making
a good impression—health food a must?—she put
me at ease during that first meeting when she ordered French toast with maple syrup and whipped
cream. Then, without any small talk, she declared,
"The business of medicine is not medicine."

"That sounds like so many other things," I
said.

"What do you mean?" she replied.

"It could be publishing, for example. Professional sports. Music, at least for those who run or-
chestras or produce recordings."

Or cancer. So vast is its insidious, multifari-
ous impact that its attendant medical and pharmaceutical infrastructure has created a kind of sub-
culture within modern, Western society. Simply to

explore the literature of this beast, as I would discover, is to plunge into the proverbial rabbit hole or to stare across a canyon of illness and care so wide that its opposite side forever recedes.

"As an oncologist," Giannoula continued, "your goal is to give your patient hope." But what form should that optimism take? How, to state the question differently, can the physician provide a therapy that is grounded not in fantasy but reality?

In medical school, Giannoula explained, a doctor is typically taught a set of algorithms: if symptom A, then drug B...if tumor X, then therapy Y.

Too often the result in cancer care, she said, was the same old standard therapy, a kind of a palliative—usually with debilitating side effects—that might in the short term bring relief but over time in most cases returned the patient to the same

Vigeland

condition in which he or she started...or worse, be-cause another regimen of the same therapy was al-most certainly not going to work.

Seeking an alternative, Giannoula said no to algorithms. Instead, in a case by case process, she sought to treat each patient on an individualized basis. Based on a genomic analysis of the patient's cancer, she prescribed a targeted chemotherapy called metronomics—smaller, more frequent dos-ages—in some cases in tandem with a more tradi-tional dosage of another drug. The result was a level of care that put the cancer into a kind of dor-mancy, enabling the patient to go on living his or her life without fear and without pain.

"I don't want my patients living the disease," she said. "I don't want them to wake up in the morning being in pain. I don't want them to wake up thinking of chemotherapy.

"I want them to wake up in the morning thanking for every new morning. Being grateful for being able to be with their children. To enjoy their grandchildren. To love their partners. To walk in the park."

Giannoula herself had traveled a circuitous professional journey. Beginning as a veterinarian in the former Czechoslovakia, she eventually migrated to Canada with her husband Petr, also a veterinarian, whom she put through graduate school, at one point working as a waitress. They had two children, both now grown adults, but they eventually divorced and he subsequently died. Before her husband's death, Giannoula in her early 30s had herself gone back to school— medical school, that is. With an initial degree in veterinary science before she settled in Toronto, she earned her M.D. in 1992 from McMaster University in Hamilton, Ontario. A residency in pediatrics and

Vigeland

a fellowship in pediatric hematology and oncology followed, both at the University of Toronto. And then in astonishingly short order while still in Toronto and soon in Boston, she found her life's calling.

She had begun focusing on angiogenesis—the process, first noted by Dr. Judah Folkman at Harvard, in which blood vessels that feed tumors are created. What if, she and a few others wondered, chemotherapy were directed not at the tumor but at those blood vessels? And what if that chemotherapy were to come in smaller doses, administered more often than traditional chemo, at regular intervals?

Thus was metronomics born, and in 2000 Dr. Klement and several colleagues in Toronto, including Dr. Robert Kerbel, published the first professional paper that extrapolated this groundbreaking idea. Three years later, Dr. Folkman recruited

Dr. Klement to come to Boston. There, she developed a clinical experimental program at the Dana Farber Cancer Institute's vascular anomalies center and Children's Hospital.

"I made detection of circulating biomarkers the focus of my science," she said. "And I discovered that the majority of angiogenesis regulators—both simulators and inhibitors of angiogenesis—are sequestered in platelet and can be detected very early in tumor growth."

Continuing her pioneering work at St. Elizabeth's Center of Cancer Systems Biology, Giannoula next became the director of a clinic at Floating Hospital, which is part of Tufts Medical Center. And the following year her research laboratory relocated at Tufts as well.

"There is an establishment that sets the rules," Giannoula said to me during our initial meeting. "The revision process"—the means by

Vigeland

which new ideas and approaches are judged—"is the status quo."

Later, she would explicate the difference between "judges" who were willing to take what she called a leap and those—the large majority— who she said would only take a step. The fear of failure—translated, she added, as a vow physicians take not to do harm to a patient—accounted for the single biggest reason that metronomics was not more widely known nor commonly used.

If a fearless destiny that led from the coastal highlands of northwestern Greece, via Czechoslovakia and Canada to Boston, defined a generosity of heart, then an ardor for the wellbeing of others drove her understanding and treatment of cancer. In a practice that had put her at the vanguard in both cancer research and care, Giannoula was a physician who in the midst of a 24/7 schedule still made house calls when a patient was not well enough to get to the hospital.

She didn't own a television and had never been to the urban mall two blocks from her condo. She hoped someday to explore her adopted country of the United States but was not, she said, a tourist. She'd stay up all night if she was in the rhythm of something she was working on. Stoically handling rejection, she was not afraid to cry. She opened her home to friends who needed a place to stay when she was away, never spoke publicly in medical jargon, and was passionate about downhill skiing, which she went at with abandon, more than once breaking a bone in a fall. It was as if her approach to life could be seen as a metaphor for the systemic basis of metronomics, itself a metaphor for the incremental revelation of an individual person's memory and experience

Vigeland

within the dynamic of a great city's power and pulse.

Some 40 years before in this same city, I spent weeks at Fenway Park doing the legwork for what became my first long magazine piece, but I never wrote about being in Fenway Park by myself one chilly April morning when Tony Conigliaro, still recovering from a beaning seven years before, was taking extra batting practice that was part of his comeback—he would later die of a stroke—and there I was by myself as he hit ball after ball over the Green Monster under a gray sky. I remember the seagulls, and the black greasepaint under each eye, how handsome he was and strong. There was no one else in the old ballpark but the man pitching to Tony—Tony C., that was how everyone referred to him—and the pitcher was a much older, former Red Sox player, Johnny Pesky, with whom

I would later talk one delightful afternoon as we sat on the steps of the dugout—the dugout!—and I asked Johnny about some of the newer, symmetrical stadiums being built around then for both football and baseball, even though the shape and the artificial turf made them poor venues for baseball.

"Fuck football," Johnny said, a phrase that the magazine which published my piece edited out. I always remembered the smile and the calm, clear, soft baritone voice with which Johnny spoke and also his kindness whenever he saw me during the many weeks I spent researching and reporting my piece, greeting me by name and wishing me good luck. I would seek him out afterwards on occasions that brought me back to Fenway for other stories, notably the epochal 1978 playoff loss to the Yankees, which I watched from a perch in the old, outdoor press box (only to return home, where a

Vigeland

telegram from the Red Sox awaited, informing me that my credentials application had been approved to cover the team in the World Series).

Over the years as I met and wrote about other Boston people and experiences, Johnny retained pride of place in a personal pantheon that eventually included Derek Bok, president of Harvard, whom I interviewed in his Massachusetts Hall office while researching my first book, and Seiji Ozawa, the longtime music director of the Boston Symphony Orchestra, with whom one extraordinary summer afternoon in the Berkshires I studied the score of Mahler's Second Symphony. Eventually, I came to think of Johnny and Derek and Seiji as members of an imaginary orchestra, among whose many other "players" were the passionate author and Harvard professor Dr. Robert Coles, in whose non-credit seminar I was a student my senior year, after the assassination of Coles' close friend, Bobby Kennedy.

I was supposed to work for Bobby back in the summer of 1968. After he was assassinated, I went to Washington anyway, living at first with some acquaintances in a cockroach infested sublet near DuPont Circle before moving in with my girlfriend (and future wife), Bonnie Stewart, who'd been staying temporarily at an apartment near the Watergate, when she was offered half of a place in Georgetown where a Pembroke classmate was house-sitting for the NBC newscaster John Chancellor. I didn't have a job, but we managed on my girlfriend's paycheck from the Smithsonian, and then in August I finally followed up with the local office of the national cutlery company that I'd been working for as a door-to-door salesman back in Boston, where I was soon to be a Harvard senior. The company was called Cutco, and I'd sold their

Vigeland

knives throughout greater Boston all during my junior year, earning enough money to keep a car at school and pay for my non-tuition college expenses.

I disliked the uncertainty of the work—you only got paid if you sold something—but I was pretty good at it, and in Washington during just a couple of August weeks I made more money than my girlfriend had earned all summer, and I even won a free TV as salesman of the month. Then, back in Boston with a thesis to write—my subject was the search for the historical Jesus—I quit, and the next time I tried to sell something it was a short story to *The New Yorker*. Three years had passed, during which I'd gotten married, taught grade school in Rhode Island, and then moved to an apartment in the back of a farmhouse on a working dairy farm in the western Massachusetts hill town of Conway, half an hour's drive from Amherst, where Bonnie embarked on a graduate program in comparative literature at the University of Massachusetts while at the same place I went through the motions of getting a master's degree in education. My real ambition was to write for *The New Yorker*, and the post-modern story I worked on the longest was set in Boston and narrated by a door-to-door cutlery salesman. I gave it a post-modern title, "Two Bassoons," which was a reference to a short scene involving some street musicians outside the Park Street MTA station, or maybe now that I reflect it had to do with a concert at Symphony Hall, where in my student life I often used to go to concerts of the Boston Symphony Orchestra on Friday afternoons, when a student rush ticket was only a dollar or two.

At the Park Street subway entrance, I had written, *the squeal of the trains made me shudder. I listened: all across the city that subterranean sound could be*

Vigeland

heard by a myriad of strangers who called Boston home. The smell in the stairway was of old cigar butts and urine. I praised the stench! I tipped my hat to the rotting apple! In the station, the air hanging over the concrete waiting platform was hot and dirty and the collective odor of food sold in little booths mixed with the redolence of human perspiration and electric engines. People were going home from work; students were going home from school; old men and women and kids with lollipops and shoppers with plastic bags were all going home. Jockeying for position, stepping on each other's feet, swearing under their breath, the figures in the maze pushed toward the tracks. There the doors of the cars creaked open, releasing one set of passengers and taking on another. More cars, more people—a surging, bulging mass, going together, their separate ways, home in the autumn night. Home—to Cambridge and Brighton, Newton and Brookline; to Dedham, Waltham, and Quincy; and, out beyond the asphalt necklace of Route 128 (crowded

A Symphony for Shelbie

with trucks and buses and commuters' cars), home to
Lincoln and Lexington and other bedroom towns.

A long sequence in the story took the narrator to the Forest Lawn cemetery where the playwright Eugene O'Neill is buried. Another was set
in Revere—Reveah!—on nondescript streets
where "single working girls" (that is how ideal customers at Cutco were defined) were "hopechest-
ing," and the idea was that a set of cutlery would
become part of a young woman's dowry, so to
speak. The true subject of my story, never published in *The New Yorker,* was the city itself and the
narrator's Icarus-like ambition not simply to come
to terms with it but in all its complexity and ambi-
guity to possess it...the crazed traffic every week-
day morning and afternoon, the planes from Logan flying right over downtown, the ancient and
very narrow streets on Beacon Hill, the smell of the
sea by the piers, the fluttering sails of boats on the

Vigeland

Charles River, the windswept plaza by the Christian Science Church (where, later, there would be fountain next to a pool with kids running in and out of the water in warm weather), the victory gardens in the Fens and the nearby soccer fields and across the street the blank space where the Rembrandt hung before it was stolen from the Isabella Stewart Gardner Museum.

Years after two of my books set in Boston were published during a period when I'd also written regularly for *Boston Magazine* (I was, at different times, a feature writer, music columnist, golf correspondent, hockey reporter, and travel editor)—I was still pondering the same questions about the city and its people, its energy, its melancholy and greatness, that I had been asking myself ever since, after a Harvard class in the history of the American Revolution or the analysis of an El Greco painting, I sat in the living room of a Revere apartment and, holding a carving knife with its patented ebony handle, extended it, handle first, to the waiting dental assistant or Filene's sales associate or legal secretary and said, "shake hands with Cutco."

When I told part of this story to Giannoula, more than a year after we'd met, she raised her eyebrows and, her eyes wide opened, looked at me incredulously.

"Really?" she said.

Did she wonder why I had shared this?

I did not ask, but I believe she knew.

Just as a particular cancer grew within the environment of a specific patient's entire body, an experience took place within the continuum of a person's entire life. Troubled thoughts about my late father, rapturous travel with a group of jazz musicians, the privileged folly of worrying about my golf handicap, the time a friend chastised me

Vigeland

for adding a kiss to a goodbye hug, the disparagement of an imperious editor who questioned what he termed my meager output, the painful confusion of my first girl friend when I told her I was taking someone else to a dance, my own lingering pain when I recognized my callousness, the time I was caught trying to steal a squirt gun from the little toy shop around the corner from my childhood house, the kindness of the shop owner who told me he believed in second chances, the milkshakes at Ho-Jo's I always ordered along with the hotdog that came in a grilled bun when my dad took me out to lunch after junior choir practice on Saturdays, *My Fair Lady* that I went to see with a girl I'd known since eighth grade the day I was accepted to college, the June night the following year when I met my future wife Bonnie at a deb party and we each ditched our dates, the long walks we took on the beach on the Canadian lakeshore, riding the

A Symphony for Shelbie

roller coaster at the amusement park on that same lakeshore when I was probably nine or ten, the August day half of my lifetime ago when the phone rang in the office of the college where I'd been working and it was the coroner in a small town in North Carolina informing me that my father had just died: everything was linked.

After my initial meeting with Giannoula, she invited me to visit her lab, which I did for the first time early that December, and within a few months I was such a regular presence that I felt accepted not just as an observer but a kind of uncredentialed member.

Invariably, I stopped as well at the Floating Hospital clinic where she saw her patients. On those visits to the hospital, I always noticed the families as I searched for a place to park my car. Often with a parent cradling his or her child, they looked in the eight-story garage for the exits adjacent to the elevator that took them downstairs and into the hospital where, if their destination was the pediatric oncology clinic, they took another elevator to the second floor.

Off hours, a hush greeted them there, as if they were entering the sanctuary of a church, while on weekdays the place was a bustling mass of humanity. A sign on the wall indicated the clinic, where the waiting room resembled a kindergarten classroom, with toys and small-size furniture for the youngest patients—a far cry from the eponymous ship that had once comprised the hospital, on the theory that the ocean air would be a healthy tonic for children who, kept offshore, would also not make others sick, as if cancer were something you could give through contact with another person.

One evening, Giannoula was worried about an 18-year-old woman whose Hodgkin's lymphoma had initially "presented" as a small lump in the area above her left breast and then, a year later, the cancer had suddenly spread throughout her body and she lay in a bed in the hospital—she had been there nearly four months—waiting for the administration of a drug that might save her but that had never before been used on someone her age, and what did she do all day? I asked, did she have visitors? I continued, and she lies in bed Giannoula repeated and her mother comes she continued and I forgot something she added, forgot something I need, she meant—we were leaving from the back entrance, which adjoined the marquee for an old theater where that day hundreds of children, mostly girls, and their parents, mostly moms, were just then exiting the theater after a showing of the musical *Annie*, and we were about

Vigeland

to cross the street to eat a light dinner at the bar of a restaurant called Abby Lane—so we turned back and went upstairs to the sixth floor, the marrow floor, where Giannoula warned me not to touch anything as I followed her to a nurse's station, and how still it was that Saturday evening, just the hum of some machines down a hall somewhere, and this was where her patient was, and how I wished I could meet her but not this evening, when if she did not soon get the drug that might help her, Giannoula said, she would die, and I stood still, felt the rhythm of my breathing and the stunned recognition that this patient could be anyone, could be one of my own children or Giannoula's, was once in a metaphorical sense my very close college friend whose leukemia presented soon after he turned 40, or my mother, dead now nearly a decade after first surviving her own cancer—of the bladder, which in her case was re-

A Symphony for Shelbie

moved surgically, so for the last years of her life she wore a urostomy bag— and all through dinner at Abby Lane I kept wondering about the young woman across the street… and so, I said to myself, if I were going somehow to honor the spirit of that young woman, of this doctor, of this city where just the year before two brothers had set off bombs near the finish line of the Boston Marathon, where in his late middle age my father was admitted as a patient at Massachusetts General Hospital, his spirit broken I eventually concluded by unspoken memories from his service overseas in World War II, and where on a far happier occasion I had taken the train in from nearby Worcester one chilly April day with my youngest child, Maren, who'd decided at the age of 12 that she was a Yankees fan and we were going to Fenway Park to see her team play the Red Sox on Patriots Day, which was also

Vigeland

the day the Marathon is run though this was several years before the bombing, and where on many
other, long-ago Sunday evenings Bonnie and I
used to take the Red Line from Harvard Square to
Park and then transfer on one of the Green Lines
two more stops to Boylston, where we looked for
an empty spot in the lobby of a hotel across the
street from the bus station from where after we
held hands and talked for another hour about the
glowing future we imagined she would make the
hour-long ride back to Providence, Rhode Island,
where her college was...if I were going to pay hom-
age to the spirit of that young woman in her room
on the sixth floor across the street, as if she were an
angel and I her acolyte, what was the thread of all
these moments, something I had been trying to
fathom at least since my father died more than 30
years ago, that I first heard when I was a child,
what it represented then and came to represent as

A Symphony for Shelbie

I grew older, life itself, its mystery, beauty, and pain, a friend who lost her father the hockey coach when we were both 13, another friend who shot himself after Christmas vacation our sophomore year, the brave family of the slain Civil Rights martyr I met on that Mississippi magazine assignment, and now all these children at Floating Hospital, I knew many of their names, their cancers, their families, directly or through Giannoula, and was it possibly what my father also experienced when he played the organ, the king of instruments many called it, and I imagined the power my father must have felt when he was playing something great, the Bach Toccata and Fugue in D minor, something that put him in touch with his sense of what unlocked the mystery or temporarily erased it or brought him face to face with it and then through it.

*

Vigeland

Since Giannoula's approach to many but not all manifestations of cancer was based on the idea of controlling it rather than eradicating it, a patient might learn to live with it—and to live longer and with a better quality of life than with conventional therapy that, with or without surgery, basically prescribed an assault of radiation and highly toxic chemicals with their many deleterious side effects. To prescribe the road not usually taken required not only her experience and expertise but courage and passion.

Through repeated visits to her clinic and lab, I kept going back over what Giannoula had first explained to me when we met. Even if after standard therapy—the maximum tolerated dose, or MTD—a tumor went into so-called remission, it was almost a certainty that it would recur and that the very drugs administered initially in the MTD would seek out cells for resistance to the previous therapy. Accordingly, and counter-intuitively, metronomics was predicated on much lower dosages, given more frequently and over a longer period of time, with a genetically targeted dosage.

As I had learned, a generation ago, the renowned surgeon at Harvard Medical School and Children's Hospital, Dr. Judah Folkman, had like other surgeons observed that tumors were always bloody. What if, Dr. Folkman conjectured, that phenomenon were not simply a clue but a key to understanding the growth of tumors? And what if, he not only postulated but finally asserted, the process—he called it angiogenesis—by which a tumor was fed and, simultaneously, rid itself of waste were a direct result of the tumor's ability to generate blood vessels?

It was a thought or conclusion, depending on one's point of view, that James Watson—one of the two scientists credited with the discovery of

Vigeland

DNA's double helix—predicted, during a "60 Minutes" interview, would lead Folkman to a cure for cancer. That never happened before Dr. Folkman's death in 2008. But by then, Giannoula—who had been working with Dr. Folkman since she moved from Toronto—was continuing to expand on an epiphany of her own: since, at its root, she understood that cancer is a kind of chaotic inversion of the very cellular division that defines life, it followed that not only the blood vessels but all the connecting vessels between a tumor's cells and the surrounding cells—the host—of a patient's body must have a direct impact on a tumor's survival. And, in her view most critically, the evident corollary—what would become the foundation of metronomic therapy and its view of cancer—was not to kill the tumor but to put it into what she called dormancy.

After a patient's genome had been mapped and a specific chemical combination prescribed and made, Giannoula's strategy for many tumors was to starve it by slowly and methodically attacking the tumor's host rather than the tumor it-self.

"For solid tumors," she explained, "many of the physiological normal mechanisms can be turned off, and that's what metronomic chemotherapy does. The target of metronomic chemotherapy is not the cancer cell...it's the blood cells, the inflammatory cells, the fibroblast, and stromal cells that secrete the tumor's growth factors."

With a rapidly growing body of validating evidence in her practice (financed for a time by grants totaling more than six and a half million dollars from organizations such as National Institutes of Health and the Binational Science Founda-

Vigeland

tion) as well as positive results of small clinical trials elsewhere, metronomics was becoming better known.

But, as I was also discovering, it was still considered by most oncologists as "experimental."

What prompted a doctor to try a new therapy? It was a question I had been asking myself ever since I met Giannoula.

"Metronomic therapy...continues to be an intriguing idea in cancer therapy and a variety of exploratory studies have suggested that it can be well tolerated," Dr. Harold J. Burstein, a breast cancer specialist at Boston's Dana-Farber Cancer Institute and associate professor of medicine at Harvard Medical School, told me. "Hopefully, ongoing trials will prove whether this approach has a regular role in treating cancer... It is not widely enough

used to generate contrarian views. It has never gotten mainstream interest in part because it has no
pharmaceutical company to champion it, and in
part because the limited results have been intriguing but not dramatic."

Echoing Dr. Burstein was Dr. John V. Heymach, professor and department chair of tho-
racic/head and neck medical oncology, division of
cancer medicine at the University of Texas MD Anderson Cancer Center in Houston.

"The discovery that the benefits of chemotherapy may come, at least in part, from the anti-
angiogenic effects of drugs—and that these effects
could be enhanced by metronomic dosing—has
had a major impact in how some clinicians treat
their patients," Dr. Heymach said, though this
shouldn't have surprised me—he, too, once
worked with Dr. Folkman. "The dogma had been
higher doses of chemotherapy would yield be

more effective at killing tumor cells and therefore yield better results, provided that toxicity could be managed. This dogma did not explain why some drugs seemed to provide benefit when given at lower, more frequent dosing. The concept of metronomic chemotherapy helped clinicians and researchers recognize that the impact of chemotherapy was often not on tumor cells— which can rapidly become resistant—but on the vasculature and other types of cells within the tumor. This has led many clinicians, including myself, to choose more frequent dosing regimens of drugs such as taxanes [plant-based chemotherapy agents] instead of maximum tolerated dosing in some situations."

Nevertheless, many doctors still had reservations. "Medical conservatism," Dr. John Sweetenham, medical director of the Huntsman Cancer Institute in Salt Lake City, Utah, called this. Though metronomics was not in use at Huntsman,

Dr. Sweetenham explained, "there have been many other developments in the last five to ten years," and he cited newer, targeted drugs, with fewer side effects and that can be taken as pills. And yet, Dr. Sweetenham continued, "the treatment paradigm is changing," and like Giannoula he noted the progress of diabetes therapy.

The lack of more flexible clinical trials also underlined the fear prompting a traditionally trained oncologist's hesitation to incorporate metronomics in his or her practice. To wit, and for illustrative purposes: if in standard chemo trial X, 10 patients were given dosage Y, it was probable that only two such patients would find benefit from tumor Z and of those two one would later experience a recurrence—and, meanwhile, all ten would lose their hair, become nauseous, and/or sleep poorly, and so on. Thus, the argument went, without even introducing metronomics into the discussion,

Vigeland

there was serious reason to reconsider a continued use of traditional chemo. Now, add targeted, metronomic chemotherapy to the trial and what did we have? To state the question differently, how could there even have been a true trial with large numbers when by definition the kind of genetic targeting to be used here was specific only to an individual patient? You would, in other words, have needed to do a "trial" of the same patient over and over again...and why, at that point, Giannoula would add, would you want to do that, even if you could, when in her experience the success rate with metronomic therapies she has used was, she said, much higher that in traditional chemo.

By that reasoning the only "safe" decision such a physician would make was to continue with the old, even if the success rate was low and en passant made those who underwent it feel worse. The use of targeted agents was also intimidating as it involved biology discovered in the last few decades and unfamiliar to many practicing physicians. It was unlikely that such a physician also had a laboratory background, a key aspect of understanding, well enough to use, the cellular frontier of such path-breaking modern medicine as metronomics.

And there was no magic bullet for cancer, Giannoula often reminded me. The genes we need to live are the very genes—mutated—that cause cancer. A cancerous tumor is not some kind of foreign body that has somehow been introduced into a person's body to wreak havoc. It is an organic part of that body, growing in a way that it should not but growing, nevertheless, because the body "thinks" the tumor is part of itself.

To bring the tumor under control, to enable the person suffering from it to live an otherwise healthy, productive life, two things had to happen:

Vigeland

the means by which the tumor grew had to be cut off, and the tumor itself had as much as possible to be eradicated. Giannoula's practice of metronomics stopped the tumor's growth in a part of therapy she termed the backbone. But to attack the tumor itself—what she called sensitizing—without killing off surrounding healthy cells required a targeting of the cancer that was much more specific than simply focusing on the body part where it happened to manifest. For such sophisticated targeted therapy, a profile of the patient's genome was the first step in a process that in her practice was becoming facilitated with the use of an extraordinary new software tool developed over several years by her son Christos, a software engineer, and two of his colleagues.

"You can know the principles of biology, but no one can possibly remember every gene and every pathway," Giannoula explained. "There are databases that scientists use. One, called STRING, enables you to put the name of a protein you have identified and then you click on home sapiens to see where the protein fits in the large scale of genes. Then, if you are a clinician, you go to a different database called NCBI/gene and you look at the gene and what it does. This tells you where it is and some of the functions, but it doesn't really give you the information that is clinically relevant.

"Yet another database tells you if there is an associative gene abnormality that results in a disease. This database describes how the gene was isolated, what it does, and what its biochemical structures are. So, in order to understand what a genetic mutation in a patient means, you have to go through all these processes. Additionally, a patient may have more than one gene mutation, in fact several are often the case."

Vigeland

The new software tool linked the various databases, including those that give information on pathways. The tool also translated different names for the same gene that have been given by scientists working in different languages around the world. Using artificial intelligence, the tool enabled Giannoula to get the directionality of a given pathway, the interaction of different mutations, the spatial organization of different pathways, the genetic phenotypes of people who have the particular gene mutation, and the use of various drugs relative to the gene mutation. After matching, cross referencing and further analysis within her own database, Giannoula was able to extract the relevant information in an almost instantaneous process that, without the new tool, might take 12 hours per patient.

Pathways within the tool were organized by high relevance to cancer, medium relevance, and low. Giannoula would make pathway choices based on many factors, ranging from the kind of cancer to the presence of growth factor abnormalities. Then the challenge was to analyze how the selected pathways interact with each other. A network of such would be created, showing how many proteins are involved in the interaction of the selected pathways.

Without the ability of the tool to extract from the complex of interactions, it would be impossible to delineate every interaction and specify which was most important. Thus, a clinician who tried to do this on his or her own would not only spend a great deal of time but eventually end up having to make an educated guess as to treatment. Even with the software tool, there would be conclusions for which there was no known available drug. Over time, as other clinicians used the tool its database

Vigeland

would grow with the input of treatment plans and their eventual outcomes.

Or such was the hope.

Back in Boston one winter's day, Abdo Abou-Slaybi handed me a pair of blue surgical gloves. A native of Lebanon who lived now in Worcester, Abdo had begun working as a lab technician for Giannoula several years earlier after someone in his family was a patient of hers. While continuing his own education, he did much of the heavy lifting in Giannoula's lab, painstakingly following complex protocols in the performance of countless experiments.

Standing behind a transparent plastic shield, he instructed me to look into the eyepiece of a Nikon microscope, which he had focused on a cell line (a strand of the same cells) he had extracted

from one of the many vials kept in a thermostati-
cally controlled, germ-free closet. Peering into this
space, magnified by a factor of 600 that, otherwise,
would be invisible to the naked eye, I beheld a
world of constantly moving and interacting dot-
like shapes that in this viewing mode were various
shades of black against a whitish gray background
cloud.

"You are looking at the living cancer cells,"
Abou-Slaybi told me then, "of a boy who died of
cancer sometime in the 1950s." Later, he would
correct himself, saying that this particular cell line
was actually from 1973 and were those of a four-
year-old girl who had neuroblastoma, a childhood
cancer of nerve cells that are not fully mature.

With or without this correction, this viewing
was no doubt for Abdo a routine experience. Nevertheless, the tone of his voice betrayed a quality
of reverence, as his own eyes widened during a

Vigeland

recitation of how such samples were acquired and stored and, most importantly, used in metronomic experiments with mice.

My mind spinning, I left the lab that late afternoon and, in part to avoid having to drive home in the heavy traffic at rush hour but mostly just to decompress, I took a long walk through much of downtown Boston, stopping once to review my notes and a second time to get something to eat. Everywhere I went the image of the lab and stories Giannoula was beginning to tell me about some of her patients resonated within my sense of the city's vastness and the complex of all these human beings—most of whom carried within us, as Giannoula would continue to explain to me in ever greater detail, probably two or three cancers that, if we were lucky, were dormant.

Such, for vivid example, had been the case for young Ava D'Ambrosio, who when she first came to see Giannoula several years ago almost looked pregnant. Ava, it turned out, was suffering with an abdomen distended by a spleen, which continued to consume fast growing blood cells that were triggered by the mutation of a growth gene called KRAS. As a consequence, Ava's spleen had ballooned to the size of a large soda bottle. Already incapacitated by a regimen of prednisone, Ava was left with bones so brittle that she broke her spinal vertebra when a classmate fell on top of her while they were playing tag.

Eventually, her condition under control with a daily dosage of thalidomide, Ava had her radiant, young life back and had even been a speaker on behalf of Giannoula's clinic. By the time I met her she was entering sixth grade, she was taking ballet lessons, playing the piano, and writing a memoir about her illness that she intended to

Vigeland

give to Dr. Klement. And, she told me when I visited one lovely June afternoon at her family's home in a suburb north of Boston, "I want other kids to know it's important not to give up." Her ambition, she continued, was to become a hematologist.

In Giannoula's practice, there had been many other successes among the nearly 60 patients she cares for annually, including some adults who have exhausted other, more conventional options. The result was somewhat like what had happened with AIDS treatment, wherein patients may still have the HIV virus, but the individually-calibrated drugs they take enable them to live productive, healthy lives.

Jenna Conley had suffered from anaplastic ependymoma, a form of brain cancer that first manifested in Jenna's life when she was only two and a half. After a long series of intricate surgeries and temporarily successful regimens of traditional chemo and radiation therapy stretching over the past decade, Jenna became a patient of Giannoula's about the time that I had met Irina Kareva. Jenna had just finished sixth grade and was about to start middle school the following fall. Her tumor seemed once again to be under control, but the medications she was currently taking had cost her hair. She was completely bald and feeling self-conscious about it.

Over time, Giannoula weaned Jenna from three of the drugs she was taking and instituted a metronomics dosage for a fourth. "'More is not more,'" Jenna's mother recalled Giannoula saying to them. "'Plants need water, but too much water can kill them.'"

By the following winter, Jenna was feeling well enough to ski with her older brother and dad, an environmental engineer. Her sibling would come along, too, but Jenna was a far faster skier, even taking on the famously steep slopes of Stowe, Vermont. And in the spring, she played on her school's lacrosse team. Though she usually wore a scarf on her head, her hair had started to grow back.

No one including Giannoula could say for certain what was next for Jenna. Nor was the prognosis of every patient resolved in the same way. Giannoula told me she remembered a teenaged girl with a different brain tumor whose father came to speak with her a few years ago.

"'Do whatever you have to do,'" Giannoula recalled the father saying, "'but please keep her alive.'"

From a large family, the girl by then had already endured several surgical procedures and standard therapies.

"'I'll do all I can,'" Dr. Klement said she replied. "'But I can't guarantee a miracle.'"

A Symphony for Shelbie

That, too, might depend on one's definition, in this case of a miracle.

For three more years, on a targeted dosage of metronomic chemotherapy, the girl went to school, kept up with her friendships, and during vacations went on family trips, including a visit to San Francisco, where she was able to cross the Golden Gate Bridge.

Then, the tumor began to grow again, and this time there was no drug or procedure that could stop its assault. Soon it would become so large that, with no space within the girl's skull to expand, the pathways that sent signals to her heart would be cut off and she would be unable to breathe. Giannoula made visits to the family's home, staying at the bedside of her patient for the last two days of the girl's life.

*

Vigeland

Driving into the city to meet Giannoula for dinner, I parked in the garage I always parked in where my friend Bobby used to work, used to let me park in one of the reserve spaces if the garage were full. No Bobby that day, wonder whatever happened to him. Not that long since I met another Boston friend also named Bobby. Bobby Joe Leaster. In the 1970s he had been picked up by the police two blocks from Symphony Hall after a store clerk had been shot and the description of the shooter was a young black man. Before Bobby Joe Leaster left prison a free man, he spent nearly 15 years in jail for a crime he did not commit. Bobby Joe worked for the city now, worked with kids in the neighbor-hoods not far from Symphony Hall.

My own connection with this building stretched all the way back to when I was six, the year my paternal grandfather died, and my then

35-year-old dad, who was the organist at a pros-
perous Protestant church and associate manager of
the Buffalo Philharmonic Orchestra, took me and
the rest of his young family to Hancock, Maine,
where the famed French conductor Pierre Mon-
teux was leading a summer conducting workshop
in which my dad enrolled as a student. On our way
from Buffalo to Maine, we stopped in Boston,
where my dad wanted to play the new organ that
had been installed in Symphony Hall a few years
before.

I have little memory of the details of that
visit, and I even wonder today how the console of
the organ could have been usable, since in my
adult experience it is not brought out on stage except during a week when the orchestra is performing a piece that includes a part for organ. I guess
my dad must have said something to someone,
which he was good at.

Vigeland

82

Imagine, in any event, that I am sitting with my father on that console, as I did on countless occasions at our church in Buffalo. Holding my three-year-old brother in her lap, our mother must have been seated in one of the front rows, main floor, of the enormous, otherwise empty, hall. Overhead, a golden proscenium—I wouldn't have noticed this then, but I have seen it many, many times since—at the top center of which is inscribed in large, ornate letters a name: Beethoven.

What did my dad play?

Probably some Bach, maybe some Buxtehude or an excerpt of Dupre or Durufle. Certainly he must also have tried at least a bit of the slow movement from Saint-Saens's so-called Organ Symphony, and then I am sure he would have ended with the entire Toccata from Widor's Fifth Symphony, a mesmerizing showpiece that he performed often at special occasions.

A Symphony for Shelbie

For late December, it was a mild night—
with the winter solstice, the longest night of the
year—but we still wore coats, buttoned or zipped
up, and I had on a hat. Earlier, we'd gone for a
glass of wine that turned into supper at an infor-
mal restaurant near the Fens, a block from the
diner where we'd first met. Ahead, I still had my
two-hour drive back to Amherst, but when Giannoula said she was going to walk Gabby I volunteered to come along. Heading down a side street
toward Mass Ave—Massachusetts Avenue—we
cut through an arcade in the condominium building that many years ago replaced the Back Bay
Theater.

"I saw Charles Aznavour here," I said.
"Back when I was in college."

"Oh," replied Giannoula, with an inflection
that implied a disinterested question, her way of
processing information without reacting to it.

Vigeland

"My wife…well, we weren't married yet, but she wanted to go." And then we crossed Mass Ave to the Christian Science "mother" church side, where in some bushes Gabby had to poop.

"There's a building I spent I lot of time in," I said, pointing toward nearby Horticultural Hall, the longtime headquarters of *Boston Magazine*. This, I quickly realized, was another non-starter, as was my nod in the other direction to the large, red-light sign for the Sheraton, a mnemonic locale from my college days (now and then I would splurge on a room for Bonnie and me), but hardly worth talking about with a doctor I'd known now for more than a year, whose work I had studied, part of whose life I had on several occasions shared, but whose inscrutability remained an inspiring challenge. Just when I was certain I finally understood what drove her she'd throw me with an aside I couldn't fathom, cite a meeting she had to attend or a call she had to take, make sure in other words that a necessary distance was always maintained, however close in our conversation we momentarily became.

A professional habit, I concluded. Like what she'd explained to me once about the impossibility of a doctor's treating a friend. Feelings would get in the way, she said. Judgment would be impaired.

After we'd briefly stopped by the old jazz club, Wally's, and looked in the window, as we neared our return to her street we came upon the brightly lit marquee and main entrance of Symphony Hall. "There's a nice concert coming up. Mozart and Bruckner," I said, gesturing toward a poster. But I added nothing more about a scene in my memory from just two months earlier, when at a rehearsal I watched as the stage door opened and the orchestra's new music director, Andris Nelsons, made his way to the podium, nodding with

Vigeland

a smile to the musicians he passed as if he were among old friends. Wasting no time on chitchat, he had looked over his left shoulder, in the direction of the assembled soloists, before beginning the music with an energy and passion that immediately dispelled any notion that this was going to be a mere run-through.

Though he also had been scheduled that day to speak at a press conference discussing the programs for the next season, none of this had appeared to be on his mind after an intermission break as he spot-checked important passages in the program. Each time after hearing what he wanted, he had said, "yes," or "thanks," and at the conclusion added, with a reference to the concert for which they were preparing, "I am really looking forward to tomorrow."

At that very moment, less than two miles away, Giannoula would have been leading a seminar in her lab. Afterwards, I learned later, she walked the few blocks to her clinic, where one of her appointments was with Shelbie Murphy, whose tumor could still be controlled but whose ability to walk was now compromised after her pelvis shattered from dancing "too hard" at a prom. Would she, Giannoula fervently hoped, somehow remain engaged with life? It was the very phrase she had used once when we were talking about Beethoven: what their worlds had in common.

Now, as we moved along on this late December night, I kidded Giannoula once again about her refusal the previous summer to attend a concert at Tanglewood, even one in which Irina was singing, because according to Giannoula that place was for—her word—"the literati." And then I remembered something she had said to me over a summer dinner during which she was explaining

Vigeland

to me the on/off "switch" of a protein that controls growth, because a classic feature of a cancer tumor is a gene mutation that has disabled this switch, leaving it on.

Giannoula reached out then and took my hand in order to lead me in conversation back to an embryonic moment when a cell began to grow in my mother's body and gradually became the end of a finger, which in turn became a finger concomitant with other fingers and a hand, ten fingers, two hands, and then an arm, two arms, and so on. Already the genetics and biochemistry and biophysics were, I realized, far more complicated than, say, the science of sending a rocket to Mars. And of course all of what she was explaining happens within a "context" of the rest of the body and the brain, and for billions of people across a seemingly infinite spectrum of vast permutation and yet fundamental consistence. And someone else's

A Symphony for Shelbie

hand learns eventually how to finger a violin, another's to hold a baseball...to treat a sick child...to reach out...grasp...and dance.

I could not help thinking just then of stories Giannoula had shared with me about her late father, Christos, after whom her son was named. Like Giannoula's mother, he was a member of the Communist party in Greece, and for many years they were both guerilla fighters against the Greek junta before being exiled in 1967.

"When he was not aiming a gun," Giannoula said, "my father was an effective communicator. Calm, patient, with a very firm sense of where he was going." She could, I thought, have been describing his daughter, a nomad who had made a temporary home for herself in a city thousands of miles from the Prague of her early childhood and the tiny hamlet of Galatas, Preveza in the coastal highlands of northwestern Greece to which her

Vigeland

parents eventually returned after democracy was restored and where, today, Giannoula still owned a house herself.

"It is a privilege, what I do," she continued. And we talked for a few minutes about wellbeing. "Healthy is pliable in the same way as normal is pliable. Normal is a state of acceptance, a population statistic. Healthy is a population statistic. If you think of the bell-shaped curve in which 90 percent of people can function in society, I don't know that healthy in Western societies is healthy for the Bushmen. We couldn't do half of their stuff. We would be very unhealthy in their society.

"So I find it bizarre to say, 'healthy.' And I think there is also this feeling in Western culture that we're fighting cancer with this sense that no one ever should die of anything. And I find that bizarre, because I find birth is healthy as is death."

A Symphony for Shelbie

Startled, dumbstruck really, as if I were listening to the friend I wished I'd had when in high school I started reading Plato's *Phaedo*, his dialogue about the immortality of the soul, and how I wondered then did I reconcile the anguish I imagined as my father at dinner one night told us about his visit with the family whose two sons had just been killed in an automobile accident, a head-on collision not with another car but an embankment that defined the end of a dead-end street, and tears formed in my father's eyes as he told us this story, and what was I to make of my mother's silent response, was it that she feared letting herself go "there," or was it I later wondered that even then she was already aware of the strange, maddening, ingratiating, touching ability her husband had of fixating on the problems of others as a way—was this really possible? dare I say it, even now?—as a way of avoiding his and their own?

Vigeland

"I think there is a way of living with cancer that is not a disease," Giannoula continued, "meaning it allows us to have mental and spiritual and societal health, and it permits us living and enjoying: that's health to me...

"And so I feel incredibly honored to be part of people's lives in their last years of life. I know I am going to lose some of them. But I am going to make it as full as I can."

II: *NIGHT MUSIC*

With chilly September evenings, autumn had arrived early in the Berkshires, and in Lars's heart. Maybe he'd make his late lunch a picnic, he thought, as he selected some cold cuts and cheese to go with a baguette, some fruit, and a Cab that was on sale at Guido's, an emporium of good cheer just north of Lenox. Then he drove back to the single-story cottage on the Stockbridge Bowl that his family's old friend Ricardo had lent Lars while he began his memoir about Gabriel, *White Boy in a Black Band*.

As Lars organized his picnic, the air was still, and there was hardly the ripple of a wave in the lake, which for some incongruous reason was called a bowl. Perhaps it was the shape as seen

Vigeland

from above—somewhat round, with many little ir-
regularities along the shoreline and one peninsula-
like protuberance, on the eastern side of which
near the rounded tip sat Ricardo's cottage. In any
event, the term had stuck, so that while in conversation a person might make reference to, "the lake,"
in the literature of the Berkshires the place was invariably called the Stockbridge Bowl.

Lars packed a blanket and an extra sweater.
Leaving the back door unlocked, he began walking. A slight breeze had come up and he could hear
the lake lapping against the pilings that held up
the dock. After an unusually hot summer, Ricardo
had left it in, since the water was still warm
enough for sailing or swimming.

Looking across part of the lake from the
dock, Lars could just see the outline of the small
beach where he and Penny had shared a picnic at
a wine tasting that Tanglewood sponsored. These

days, there were many such events to lure more customers for the concerts the orchestra presented during a festival that now ran from mid June until early September, though the orchestra itself played only on weekends in July and August. The wine tasting coincided with a student production of a Mozart opera, but they skipped the music.

Most of the neighbors had closed their cottages for the season and moved back to their city homes, but Lars could see from the open windows in his house that Rothman was still around. Once a famed virtuoso, Rothman had mysteriously lost his musical memory in a notorious concert several years ago at Chicago's Ravinia Festival. Since moving to the Berkshires, he'd become something of a local historian, as if focusing somehow on other matters would enable him to rediscover his command of the piano and restore his prominence as a world-class performer.

Vigeland

More than once Lars had responded to a question about himself by saying, "I am actually a musician, but I don't perform because I didn't practice enough when I was growing up." It was an effective way of avoiding the truth, he'd discovered, and not only about writing but also about life.

Ten years ago, just as a long project on which he had been collaborating was finally taking shape, Lars resolved to rethink a career that he was forever viewing as slow in its formation and late in its achievement. Another ghosted book, several sexy magazine assignments, and two more years would pass before an event in his family shook him out of his procrastination: his gifted daughter Rachel, 14 at the time, ran away, first for just a day and then for nearly a month. She was eventually found, but the shock of her temporary disappearance and the loss of his parental innocence forced upon Lars a reappraisal of his life that he had been promising but for one reason or another putting off.

"Don't beat yourself up," he could hear any number of people he knew telling him. As if such thoughts were something he could turn on and off. Nothing in his life consciously escaped his attention. Every book, every person, every day, every song: he wanted to possess them all, attesting to a truth that the present seemed to be telling him: if grace were real, it was getting late to affirm what he had found many times before, only later to lose, backstage in clubs and other venues, where he often listened alone, standing on the side of the stage, behind a portion of the drawn curtain, and in the thousands of people he had met, the many miles—often late at night—traveling from city to city in Gabriel's tour bus...with changes in the weather, the sky, the topography...the voices of

Vigeland

98

band members behind him as he sat often on the little stool by the driver's seat...the arrival in another place and the waiting in the bus while the Chief checked them in and then came back onto the bus to distribute room keys...soon he was unpacking...and then they were off to the venue for soundcheck...and he often met someone then and they'd talk since he was the one in the band not playing...there would be a meal, usually backstage, sometimes back at the hotel...then the gig...afterwards, people would congregate, always in good spirits, Gabriel often giving an impromptu lesson to a young trumpeter who came to the gig with his parents and his horn...he was usually the last to leave, with him, often carrying his trumpet...back to the hotel they went, maybe for some sleep or if the next gig were a long drive they might leave at two or three in the morning. How he loved the feeling of traveling through empty

A Symphony for Shelbie

streets, imagining the lives of all those sleeping men and women, imagining their awakening and they would be several hundred miles someplace else and it would begin again, the same sequence though it was always also different, and all this while his children at home, growing, Penny wondering, his friends and other family always curious and they would come to the gig when the band was in a place where they lived, he would leave them tickets, and then a break and home and trying to re-find that rhythm, always took a few days, and just as that began to feel normal again it was time to leave again.

Following the winding gravel driveway to its intersection with Makheenac Road, Lars turned left and walked north toward the entrance to Wheatleigh. Now a pricey hotel, Wheatleigh was originally a Gilded Age mansion, but when Lars was a

Vigeland

boy its carriage house and barn were briefly the site of a jazz school and jazz concerts. Later, as the Music Inn, it morphed into a venue for folk, pop, and rock before complaints about the noise and the crowds led to its closing and eventually, under new ownership, the incongruous development of a condominium complex.

Turning west, on what was now called Hawthorne Road, he soon continued past the corner on the right of Hawthorne *Street*—go figure—which marked the beginning of the Tanglewood property. Just then, a mysterious sound startled Lars. He was sure he had heard three notes, distant but distinct, like the beginning of a bugle's call at a cemetery. Standing still, he waited for something more, but there was nothing except the soft whoosh of a breeze. He must be dreaming, he concluded, since the summer music season was over. Perhaps it was just a sound in his head, reminding him of a story that stemmed from the encounter with a bird—an eagle? a falcon?—that Gabriel was supposed to have had as a teenager during a walk in the woods at a summer music camp he attended in North Carolina. With Gabriel was a woman a few years older, a New Jersey woman who had spent part of her childhood in India and who would eventually become a healer. Off they went on a walk and soon found themselves in a forest clearing where they took seats—on the ground? a fallen tree?— and Gabriel began to whistle. But instead of the notes to a song the sounds he made were a kind of call: a summoning from within of a chord, C-F-G, and suddenly as he whistled the bird appeared, at first flying overhead and then, finally, as it alighted on one of Gabriel's outstretched arms, singing...C-F-G.

Soon, on the left side of the road, Lars passed the replica of the red farmhouse in which—as

Vigeland

Rothman had recounted a few days ago—Nathaniel Hawthorne wrote *The House of Seven Gables* in 1850. The pump for the well Hawthorne himself may have used still stood near one side of the present farmhouse, which looked out at its other end on a meadow through which, Rothman had continued, Hawthorne frequently walked on summer mornings with his son Julian down to the lake— the very meadow over which Lars gazed now, more than a century and a half later.

Hawthorne had moved to the Berkshires with his wife and children after being forced to leave Salem upon the publication of his *Scarlet Letter*, which had caused a scandal among the gentry, as if to deny that their ancestors had burned supposed witches. He was introduced to Herman Melville on a picnic hike in August 1850. Melville, in his early 30s and more than a decade younger than Hawthorne, bought a farm in nearby Pittsfield shortly after that first meeting. It was here, across from Tanglewood in the original of the red farm-house—destroyed by fire in 1890— that he and Hawthorne talked over brandy about *Moby Dick*'s evolution throughout the fall and winter following their introduction.

Late the next year, a week before Hawthorne left the Berkshires for Concord, never to return, Melville invited him to lunch at what was then called Wilson's Hotel in the center of Lenox. With a porch that wrapped around the corner formed by its two front sides, facing the main intersection in Lenox, Wilson's for much of its later history would be known as the Curtis. An outside stairway near the porch railing led for many years to a basement bar, a gathering spot where tourists mingled with musicians amidst the ghosts of Nathaniel and Her-man and of other, later luminaries, including Edith Wharton and her pal Henry James.

Vigeland

Lars remembered tagging along with his brother one summer night and having a drink there with a famous conductor whose primary interest was sizing up whom in the room, male or female, he might sleep with. Upstairs from the bar, a wide hallway with a high ceiling trimmed with ornament-like woodwork led to the dining room, now a pharmacy. In that very place, just before Thanksgiving in 1851, Herman presented to Nathaniel a copy of his great book, which had just been published and which began with an effusive dedication to the older author. To Melville's deep regret, they would meet only twice more before Hawthorne's death in 1864.

Reaching the end of Hawthorne Road, past the tall hedge that bordered the Tanglewood property, Lars made a right onto the state highway and soon another right into the main Tanglewood parking

A Symphony for Shelbie

lot. Carrying his picnic stuff in a knapsack, he quickened his pace as he neared the Tanglewood entrance. His first glimpse of the grounds through the distant gate reminded him of a course he'd recently played with his golf pal Francois. They'd had dinner afterwards on the clubhouse deck, where they talked for another hour, Francois sipping cognac as he looked up at the night sky and saying how little their lives were in the context of the immensity above, stars that had been there for millions of years, and Lars with his cognac paraphrasing the end of Proust, after the narrator has had his last reunion with Gilberte and World War I has ended and so, too, readers realize will the narrator's life, but the very long book lives, how while we are alive we are giants in the dimension of time.

Francois was always thinking several thoughts ahead. It was one of the reasons he'd

Vigeland

turned his father's small repair business into a very profitable machine parts factory, and then why the restaurant he started after he sold the factory a few years ago became such an immediate success. He'd sold that, too, which was how he was free to play hooky with Lars. Less clear was where or how Lars found the time, given the somewhat precarious state of his life.

"Come on," Lars remembered saying impatiently to Francois before he'd won their match with a miracle bogey on the 16th hole and an even more improbable par on the 17th. The long, hilly walk around the course had tired Francois to the point of apparent exhaustion, and then he suckered Lars into trying a shot on the 16th he knew Lars couldn't make, which should have been a clue, not that it really mattered. They weren't playing for anything.

"Suppose we had a huge bet going," Lars had said in the gathering dusk as they approached the 17th green, near a pond in the woods beyond which was hidden a log cabin. The dreamer who'd founded the course had briefly lived there. He'd died years ago, his ashes interred in the village cemetery a mile away, and the cabin was now the office of the architect who designed the course. An old Yale grad who still smoked a pipe, he'd come over to chat with them in the pro shop before they'd teed off. Lars had tried to persuade him to join them, but he pled too much work, which he began to describe in such detail that Lars worried they wouldn't have time to play a full round.

Virtually the only people on the course that afternoon, they had played quickly if not well, with Francois taking the front nine. Rallying, Lars won four of the first five holes on the back, when he began talking about ghosts the course reminded

Vigeland

him of: the woman, a former neighbor, he'd played with once when the course was only nine holes, and the loose-fitting, low-necked shirt she wore with no bra, and how she'd beckoned him to help her look for a ball she'd lost in a thick grove of trees along what was now the 12th hole, and when she bent over he could see her breasts, which seemed like a different kind of beckoning but the moment passed; the long-ago Thanksgiving morning when his brother and he had played, even though the course was officially closed, and it was so cold that the pond on the par-three 15th was frozen, and they'd skipped their tee shots off the ice.

"Suppose in a story someone who had known this place had come back here," Lars had said to Francois as he tapped in his putt on the 17th. "Suppose that someone were me, except I wasn't the me who is talking and playing golf with you right now but a guy who lived, I don't know,

A Symphony for Shelbie

maybe up in Vermont during the summer and then somewhere south in the winter, Florida or the Caribbean. Maybe this guy used to play on the pro golf tour or tried to, something happened to him, maybe longer ago. Maybe he was once a hockey player before he got into golf and something happened, something awful."

"Like he killed someone," Francois said. "Hit a little kid with a puck and killed him." And then, "Where is the last tee? And I thought you told me the architect's house was here."

"It's not his house, it's his office. There, through those trees." And then Lars had led Francois in the other direction, up a short incline, to the tee for the 18th.

"Like the puck idea," Lars said, and he wondered if it had come from Francois's relatives in Quebec, except he knew Francois hadn't played much hockey.

Vigeland

"Later," Francois said. "Let me bust you with this drive," and he almost came out of his shoes, he swung so hard, sending his ball to the left of an outcropping of trees and rocks. "Where is my fade when I need to hit it right?" he said, but Lars wasn't really paying attention. Francois had already won the match, and it was almost dark and chilly.

The next morning, they had breakfast at the café Francois had founded, each man with a blueberry muffin, Francois's a diet version, and over Lars's coffee and Francois's green tea, Lars said something about a story he been had working on that started in Berkeley with his search for a jazz place that he discovered finally was gone and all that was left was its sign, the same day of his meeting with a woman who quoted a poem about the need for people to give up the worlds to which they do not belong, and how presciently would he

A Symphony for Shelbie

come to view that advice, but how, he would ask himself, before giving up such a world were you to recognize it? Perhaps the story would provide a "place" he could go to and "people" he could be with—wishing everyone a calm day if that is possible, praying that they will remember you cannot do it all and that once you're out from under most of that "all" doesn't seem to have mattered that much. "Treasure your memories," Lars would say to himself, their buoyancy, what you have learned from them about mortality, often a painful lesson but also as long as he was in possession of his faculties a lasting one, stitching together the context within which he kept believing he was forever on the precipice of discovering at long last the meaning he had been searching for since he was a boy, listening to the sounds of his father's songs.

*

Vigeland

Now, at the Tanglewood entryway, fading posters displayed information about the final events of the recent music festival. There was not another person in sight. The scene reminded Lars of something he'd written, years before, about this very spot, a book's beginning that his editor cut— inexplicably, to Lars's ear: *Flapping in a light breeze, five sun-faded flags flank an American atop the roof of the main entrance gate at Tanglewood. A single car occupies a lonely space in the parking lot. The closed gift shop displays posters of music director Seiji Ozawa, Tanglewood sweatshirts in gray, green, and purple, Tanglewood pink and blue knit shirts, and many other souvenirs, including Tanglewood "engineer's caps." Past the shop and through the gate, open until sunset, water sprinklers send their spray into the quiet air, fragrant of early autumn. Beyond the vast lawn's horizon, the leaves in a few of the trees have started to show some seasonal color. The famous Tanglewood Shed, the eaves*

A Symphony for Shelbie

of the old auditorium creaking in the wind, stands
empty.

Lars let himself in and walked up the path
toward the main Tanglewood house, built according to Rothman by Hawthorne's temporary Lenox
landlord, the Tappans, around the time of the Civil
War. Continuing along the path, past the house, he
headed in the direction of what was once the main
entrance to the former estate, guarded on both
sides by the statues of lions that gave the entrance
its name, and walked further toward the adjacent
property, the site of the first Lenox "cottage," Highwood, where—Rothman again—the Tappans
lived initially when they came to the Berkshires.
Spreading his blanket under a tree on a part of the
immense lawn, he could see past the hedge and
across the road to the lake by which he was temporarily living and past that still further the distant
summit of Mount Everett. During an idyllic period

Vigeland

before the Second World War, his father lived near by, playing the organ, teaching, conducting and one summer studying here at Tanglewood.

Sitting on his blanket, Lars poured himself a glass of wine and made a silent toast. Had he lived past his early 60s, his father would have celebrated his 99th birthday this year. Momentarily lost in the melancholy of this thought, Lars was startled when his meditation was augmented by a sound he had not expected. Here on this dappled lawn, beneath a canopy of trees with leaves that were still green, he was sure he could again hear three notes that seemed this time to be coming from the direction of the main Tanglewood venue, the so-called Shed where the orchestra presented its summer concerts. Lars nibbled on some of his bread and cheese and was about to peel an apple when he heard the notes once more. Impossible! But the sound was clear and louder.

A Symphony for Shelbie

Leaving his things, he began to walk toward the Shed. Benches for auxiliary seating had been brought inside, and he had to climb between two of them to get into the enormous, empty area. The stage was dark, with little of the late afternoon light reaching it. He sat down near the back, his heart pounding.

As mysteriously as they had started, the notes stopped. Then, from across the Shed, came a new sound that quickened his pulse and startled him to attention: the whisper of human breath.

Peering in the growing shadows of late afternoon, Lars saw the stooped figure of what appeared to be an older woman. She had a large head with just a little hair, and she seemed to be staring at Lars.

She stared at him without recognition, as if she could not really see him. He stared back. Who was she? What had brought her here? And why

Vigeland

did she bear such a close resemblance to the saintly Miss Snapworth, his high school Latin teacher who had called him up to the front of her classroom once, after he had fallen in love his senior year and stopped doing his homework, and looking him directly in the eye, asked him a simple question: "What happened?"

Standing now in the back of the Shed, Lars walked toward the mystery figure, but as he got closer, it began to become blurry. By the time he reached the approximate spot where he thought it was, the apparition of Miss Snapworth had disappeared. Alone in the Shed, he remained motionless, took several deep breaths, held his eyes closed and then reopened them. Nothing but empty seats and a few birds. Slightly disoriented, he retraced his steps to his picnic place. After this strange interruption, he guessed that he had at most an hour before he'd need to pack up and go.

A Symphony for Shelbie

Lars had been coming here for concerts and picnics since he was an infant. Faded family photos show him sitting on his mother's lap in the rear of the Shed during a performance. When Tanglewood first opened, she told him, women who arrived wearing slacks were given skirts by an usher before they could enter the Shed, with its dirt floor and exposed beams, its poor sightlines and funky acoustics. More nostalgic than annoyed, she remembered that concert-goers on the lawn were attentive to the music, in her view so unlike the crowds that flocked to the place later, particularly on Sunday afternoon, wearing beach clothes and reading the Sunday *Times*. Lars's father laughed affectionately at her recollection, shaking his head and smiling, as if to redirect her reflective disposition. Unfazed about anything in a space where he

Vigeland

behaved as if he were the owner, he treated every-one else at Tanglewood as if they were guests in his home.

To be with him, to walk backstage with his father, whether he was playing or just visiting with musicians he knew, was such second nature to Lars that he never really grasped how exotic this world must have appeared to what was colloqui-ally referred to as "the audience." Lars was his fa-ther's private audience, but most of his listening and watching as a boy took place offstage. He barely paid attention when his father was actually performing.

Before they settled in what his mother thought was going to be the backwoods of Buf-falo—it turned out otherwise—the family moved around a lot, especially after Lars's dad started get-ting part-time, short-term teaching gigs at schools that wanted to be hip. Long before it became fashionable, he let his hair grow, and when his mom started ragging her husband about it he put it in a ponytail. "Hank," Lars can remember her kidding him, "who do you think you are, some hippie or something?" He would pretend not to hear her.

Now, with the sun beginning to disappear behind the mountain top to the west, the lawn in front of Highwood seemed a stage for a concert in which Lars's dad would be accompanied by the wind in the trees. Then, as if on cue, after Lars poured himself another glass of wine, he again heard the three notes, this time from a different direction and somewhat muted.

Momentarily immobile, he looked across the lawn to his left, where shadows were beginning to form on a kind of ridge above the second Tanglewood venue, a newer building built of brick and shaped somewhat like an enormous barn. The

Vigeland

building was closed, but Lars was certain the notes he had just heard came from within it.

Holding his wine glass, he headed toward the ridge, keeping close to the thick stand of tall shrubs along the edge of the lawn that formed a curtain between Hawthorne Road and the Tanglewood grounds. There, with a shudder and a pang, Lars saw standing among the remains of what must have been an apple orchard his childhood friend Eli. Until they were 12 or 13, Eli and he went to the same school, and Eli's family's house was just a couple of blocks from Lars's. Lars would walk over after he'd finished his homework and piano practicing, sometimes stopping on the way at the corner pharmacy where he might buy a candy bar and peak at the nudie magazines. Unlike Miss Snapworth, the figure that confronted him here did not seem to be looking at him, in fact it, or he, barely had a countenance.

A Symphony for Shelbie

Years ago, back in Buffalo for his brother's wedding, Penny and he had stayed in the home of one of his dad's wealthy Buffalo friends, someone whose quixotic projects included a lookout tower for tourists at Niagara Falls. In the back of the house was a swimming pool to which Lars's dad had been given a key, because like so many others the pool owner sought his dad's company. Lars and his siblings would drive over with their dad during hot summer days in the city and swim.

One of the friend's daughters was an angel in the Christmas pageant at the church where his father hired a brass ensemble hired to play holiday music. Lars wondered if angels wore underwear. Another daughter, who took singing lessons with Lars's mother, was with Eli the night before he left Buffalo following another, later Christmas and instead of driving back to college checked into a rural motel and shot himself.

Vigeland

What must have happened in Eli's life to bring it to such a painful, early end? How could he have done this to his family and his friends, many of whom received letters after his death that he had mailed before pointing that gun at his head? And why, Lars had often selfishly asked myself, was he not one of the people Eli had written?

His reverie was cut short when it appeared that the ghost of Eli was moving toward him with a gun, its barrel in Eli 's right hand pointed down. Lars took a step backwards.

Standing still, Eli smiled at him. "What did you think I was going to do?" he asked. "How can you be frightened? I faced a much greater fear when I pulled the trigger on myself."

"No," Lars said. "Living is also hard, knowing that at any moment something or someone may be taken from you."

Just as he said this, a light within the building below them came on and then went off, flashing three times before it returned to dark again. And the image of Eli was gone.

"Oh my long-ago departed friend, forgive me my trespass. You were too young to leave us. I see you now with that perpetual twinkle, a feigning mischievousness I mistook for joy. What inner hell were you escaping? And then, later, that your father would do the same thing? Who would have thought? I remember that time we rode to the beach on your motorcycle, parking it near the crowded tennis courts to achieve maximum effect. How jealous I was of the attention you received, a couple of the girls coming over to gaze at and touch the machine. Who found you that cold January night? Who touched you then and carried your cold body...where? I do not even know where you were buried, though I can hear in my

Vigeland

head the hymn from your funeral, the tune taken from *Finlandia*, 'Be still my soul.'"

Alone again, Lars waited for another flash, listened for another note. Nada. Then he looked at his watch and realized that the gate through which he had entered had probably been locked. Walking back to his picnic blanket, lost in a maze of memory and music, he wondered if a security guard might find him in this labyrinth of foliage and flowers.

As he approached the old house where Hawthorne once regaled the children of his hosts with one of his Tanglewood tales, whose were those voices?

"It is as if you could overhear and understand what the trees are whispering to one another," the first voice said, "as if you caught a glimpse of a face unveiled, which veils itself from every willful glance."

A Symphony for Shelbie

"Ah, yes, Nathaniel," the second voice responded. "All this mixes with your most mystic mood...fact and fancy, half-way meeting, interpenetrate, and form one seamless whole."

"Indeed, Herman. The mystery is revealed, and after a breath or two, becomes just as much a mystery as before. "

How long had Lars been standing there? And why, as quickly as these voices came to him, were they gone?

Lars shook his picnic blanket and folded it, put in his backpack the food and wine he had not finished, and finding no place to throw away his trash packed that, too. A half moon was beginning to rise over the lake, its dim light shining within the arbor of trees that separated the Highwood side of Tanglewood from the Shed, through which he planned to walk on his return to the main gate,

Vigeland

which he presumed he could climb over if it were indeed locked.

Just as he reached the backside of the Shed, with an open area defining the arched perimeter between the rear seats and the lawn, a light over the stage came on, revealing a solitary man holding wires and cables. Lars immediately recognized him as Robert, sound person extraordinaire in Gabriel's band. What reason could have brought him here? What, Lars asked himself again...what had prompted him to give up precious parts of his own family life to chase the echo of a horn in night clubs and concert halls across a large landscape?

He took a seat, near where he had seen Miss Snapworth earlier. It was odd, he thought, that only a single light was shining, as if a special soloist were about to appear and in the focus on that figure an expectant hush would come over the thousands typically sitting during concerts in the

Shed and on blankets or folding chairs outside. The hush was instead silence, and the anticipation of the moment was framed for Lars by the purposeful, habitual movements of the amazing Robert, whose knowledge of the intricate complex of microphones, wires, and speakers was matched during a performance by his dexterous manipulation of the soundboard's dials and levers. He worked steadily and methodically. When it came time to test the components, he hopped off the stage and walked toward the center of the Shed's box seats—folding chairs marked off by a railing—where his soundboard stood. Though no musicians had appeared on stage, he fussed with something as if in preparation for the beginning of some music.

During all his many years traveling with Gabriel—Lars would tell people he played second trumpet, in a band that for many years had only

Vigeland

one—this setting up of the stage was always his favorite time. It usually took place in the late afternoon, often only an hour or less since they had arrived from wherever the band had been playing
the night before. How he loved those lazy minutes
after a long drive as they came into a new city or
town, passing people waiting to cross at street corners, watching others going into and out of shops
and stores, seeing men and women through office
windows hunched over desks or standing, con-
versing...perhaps about the show they were going
to see that night, for which they'd bought tickets
months ago, when Gabriel was but a name in an
announcement or advertisement.

And then, after walking over or being trans-
ported via van or limousine, Lars and these musicians with whom he was traveling the country
would be in the club or hall, always by some vapid
language identified as "the venue." Robert's setup

would already be well underway, but it typically continued as the band members sauntered in, unpacked their instruments, and after tuning and trying a few notes, a scale, a riff, began to interact musically with one another, not yet rehearsing within the rubric of soundcheck but simply playing whatever came to someone's mind, and the others would join in.

Just like now, he'd be sitting somewhere, even on the stage (though never, with one rare exception in California, playing). He would open the small reporter's notebook he always carried with him and scribble something about a stagehand in the background or a joke someone in the band had just told or something he remembered from where they'd stopped for breakfast hours ago. The ostensible purpose of such note taking was to enable him later to reconstruct a scene in the biography of Gabriel that he kept putting off. The act of writing was a way of legitimatizing his presence in the guarded, private world of the band, but it was also a cover for where the music took him.

"Curtain above stage is dark blue," Lars would write, but he was actually thinking about the red dress that his date wore at their senior prom.

"Piano seems slightly out of tune," he might record, while what he was remembering was the day after, when she told him she never wanted to see him again.

Then some music would begin and new layers of what his agent called "reveals" would unfold, how he truly felt about different people would be unmasked, what he honestly saw when he looked within himself unveiled.

Where had Robert gone? The Shed was empty again, but overhead on one of the large-screen, HD

A Symphony for Shelbie

monitors recently installed to give people in the rear sections a better view of the stage, a man could be seen boarding a flight from what appeared to be Logan Airport in Boston. With a yellow and blue Burton backpack, he took an aisle seat in an exit row. As he turned in the direction of the camera, Lars shook his head in silent disbelief: the man on the screen…was he, several years ago. Soon, as the roar of the jet engines receded after takeoff, he could be heard speaking, as if this scene were part of a movie, set where that traveler had been headed, and the monologue was a voiceover.

"Up early, came over to Berkeley before the rest of the household was awake, fed the cat I'm supposed to be taking care of and read my email. Had coffee with woman I'd met at a Chicago book event almost a decade ago. Fortyish, invited Gen to attend a dance meditation class in Sausalito on

Sunday morning. Very holistic, sweet, great pickup on anything I said about life and lit.

"Met my college roommate after lunch for long walk around Berkeley campus, where he teaches. Back afterwards to the cat, in whose owner's house I am now sitting, now at dinner place, still in Berkeley, waiting for Larry and daughter-in-law, her grandparents' treat. I will tell them about driving by the site of the jazz club nearby where I sat in at rehearsal in 1992—only time I ever tried to play with Gabriel's band— gone now, very evocative, stirring really, building is now a gym but the old sign was still there, near the bay, the living breathing pulsing world, am surrounded by it here, all the people at this restaurant where I have arrived early, at the bar having a...Martini...and outside the night awaits, and I remember, what Gabriel said one night in Colorado about his horn: that you have to blow the beauty into it."

A Symphony for Shelbie

Continuing to listen, Lars remembered something else Gabriel had said, long afterwards, as if in anticipation. "You never know when something's going to end," Gabriel reminded the members of his big band at a New York City rehearsal before they went out on the road again. He had just stopped his musicians after the introduction to an Ornette Coleman tune and said in a voice barely louder than a whisper that they sounded complacent, too used to playing with one another. Some seat shifting and murmuring followed before Gabriel continued, this time to respectful attentiveness.

Lars felt somewhat awkward hearing this, as if he were listening in on—what to call this? a monologue?—that was not intended for him. Or was it in fact the opposite, that he knew only too well that this part of his life had already come to

Vigeland

an end and his continued presence was a failed refusal to accept a truth Gabriel had shared, when Gabriel had told Lars that he, Lars, had reached the point in his life that Gabriel called consolidation. What had Gabriel meant by that? What other hints had he been trying to give Lars? By what words might Lars finally grasp that though for years he had been *with* them—the band—he was not *of* them?

Whatever these beings, Lars felt, that comprise ourselves, our bodies, our souls, we are alive in the moment, seeking an echo of our happiness, the recollection of someone's touch, voice, eyes, his presence or hers. That word—echo— made reference to something Gabriel had said to him early in his touring as a kind of non-playing member of his bands: "When something is great, it echoes, and each echo is bigger than what it came from. Think of the sound of a bagpipe in a battle. Or go to the

A Symphony for Shelbie

edge of a canyon and shout, 'hello!' The major function of your existence is to do something that will ricochet, like the echo of your voice from that cliff."

Instead, Lars kept hearing echoes, like the ghosts that were visiting him this night. Here was another: twenty years ago in Greenville, South Carolina, he began a conversation during a sound-check at Furman University with a beautiful young woman…call her Kathy…who was the go-between for the school's presentation of Gabriel's septet. It was her job to make sure everything was in place. As they spoke off to the side of the stage while the band was playing, Lars realized she knew very little about jazz but was curious, and so he started in with what even then were already a large cache of Gabriel stories, and afterwards, as the band left to change and have dinner before the gig, he ended up walking back with her—he could

Vigeland

not now remember the route, but they crossed the campus—and "Would you like to get some coffee?" he asked, and, "Sure," she said, and at a café to which she led him the conversation transposed personally among other things to families, and he mentioned his dad, said he was stationed near there, in Spartanburg, before going overseas in World War II, and then years later lived briefly just over the border in Tryon, North Carolina, where he died—Lars could feel his presence, he said, as they had come into town earlier on the band's bus—and Kathy told him she saw her father infrequently, he was a riverboat captain she said. At the gig that night they sat in chairs on stage behind the pulled curtain, where they could see the band and the band could see them but the audience could not. This was a common seating and listening experience for Lars but a first for Kathy. She seemed stunned by the power of the music, especially

A Symphony for Shelbie

heard so close, saying it had taken her to a place she did not usually go.

Back at that New York rehearsal, Gabriel's alto saxophone player, two rows ahead of where Gabriel sat, kept his gaze ahead, but his body shifted slightly back and forth, as you might listening in church to a preacher's prayer or in an audience to a tune that got under your skin. The first trombonist, right behind Gabriel, did turn and look at his bandleader as he made a crack about the excellence of the trombone section. Gabriel's drummer, who was positioned to Gabriel's immediate right, seemed to be meditating on a spot in the ceiling.

"Your job is to make the person next to you sound great," Gabriel said. "Maybe this is the last day we play together. You need to play like it might be that last day."

*

Vigeland

"Spent today in Berkeley at my cat's house," the voiceover continued, "and will pickup Larry at the BART station around six with takeout pizza. Had lunch at the same diner I used to go to back when I was out here twice in the mid-nineties working on a book, actually have been to the diner three times during the week.

"Ate the same Rueben sandwich each time.

"My wife wonders what next. Rachel writes me about a school problem. My sweet son said dinner tonight was his treat. Gen embraced me when she left for the airport and said with energy and love, 'See you at home again in three weeks!'

"And I sit now in the back fenced-off mini patio garden of a Berkeley cafe, drinking French Roast, the unread *New York Times* on the table before me, and I will leave shortly for Larry's and shower and change and head over with Larry's golf clubs to the Tilden Park golf course for the afternoon, and tomorrow before I head to the airport I will have lunch with him in the city and see his office."

What time was it?

Lars could see from his seat that it was now dark outside the Shed. He should have been going but he felt immobilized.

Someone in chinos and a pullover jacket appeared on stage and removed from a satchel he was carrying a mysterious object, with which he began fussing.

As Lars watched intently from his distant perch, the person on stage set a second object on his lap, touching a button or some such, and suddenly the first object took flight.

Vigeland

It was, Lars realized, a remote controlled model airplane, though it also fluttered, like the wings of a bird...or the wings of an angel.

"Who cares," Lars thought, "what someone else thinks or says about what you have done, as in what in the world do they know"—a problem of his own that in a certain way he still fought some-times—"but really, truly," he said to himself, "choose not only your issues but your confreres, it was and forgive the analogy a little at its core, whether body or soul, like sleeping with the en-emy, it is a person's self, his or her sacred self, and for sure as soon as you share something really good a vulture will be there to steal what it can and leave you empty and thinking you failed, right when you already succeeded. It is in so many ways like love, the painful 'part,' as in the pain is always there, somewhere beneath the surface, a kind of lost chord."

A Symphony for Shelbie

Three notes: it was all there, when connected to here, as in within, what we each
carry...what Lars carried all those years on the
road and then brought home with him and then
when he left again took with him some new part
of home, they were intertwined, sitting behind the
curtain that gig with Kathy he could be thinking
about Eli, his dead friend's face forming with
Kathy's and Gabriel's a kind of visual chord, there
were infinite combinations from his life, what he
saw, what he felt, or what just recently he heard as
if by Proustian chance in Hanover, New Hampshire, where Gen and he were having a quick coffee before he left her off at the White River bus station—such resonance—and there it was, the echo
of friendships (his college roommate, whose step-
father was once the local Episcopalian priest), trav-
els (skiing nearby), music—at least two but he
thought maybe three Gabriel/Hanover trips, the

Vigeland

last of which was also one of the very last, when somewhat impulsively he drove up, it turned out, in his bedroom slippers, and there was a late night drink with a few of the band members and then after coffee the drive home...and he remembered snow that day, even though it was only October, and how cold it was outside, when one of Gabriel's saxophone players walked him to his car, all his senses were on high alert, the temperature, the clearing sky, his heartbeat, because he was alone that night, once again, and there was in his life another version of this chord...a human chord, perhaps dissonant but no less true, composed of more than one person, one found, one lost, and himself...and how, he wondered, to write that, the feeling of it, without hurting the people he loved, perhaps in a sequence that still began in Tanglewood, late this past summer, with a rehearsal for the Beethoven Ninth, but then continued with a

A Symphony for Shelbie

different series of events, ranging from Mahler Five in Boston to a concert in New York at which one of his brother's pieces was performed to a new year's gig at Smith College wherein he heard in person an astounding guitarist; and so he heard this again last summer, as by chance he found on the radio Handel's *Eternal Source of Light Divine*, and maybe the real search in all this was how to find a way to say to whomever would listen—and just to keep it to music—that stories about musicians, or doctors...teachers...are, finally, however well told, just that...stories... and if not well told they were simply information, but either way they were not the thing itself, the jism of the experience, the rush of feeling, the sense of apprehension of a thing, of beauty, of sadness, life, and so, when Lars thought about his father, or Eli, or Penny, started another story about one of them, it was as a way in, an entrance, to that thing itself, the heart of the

Vigeland

matter, what was actually within: the fight the couple on the lawn had before the concert and the memories of the old man in the last row in the Shed and the 80year-old lady with the huge hat who had been a Tanglewood usher for 20 years who told Lars that her late husband was some kind of cousin of Lenny's, the way the wind felt crossing the Tanglewood lawn at night in a light rain and how the place looked in the winter when the sides were boarded up with plywood and all this green expanse was white, a sunlit afternoon as he stopped at a nearby college, where he had often squirreled himself in the library to write, but on a certain September day it was so warm he took a seat on one of the wooden chairs on the quadrangle that looked out toward the hillside where his wife and he and their three-month old son once shared a picnic years ago and Lars thought he held the whole world in his hands.

A Symphony for Shelbie

She was standing near the back corner of the Shed, stage left, when the rain began. No wind, and just a light mist at first. It must have been almost midnight. Marvin Gaye had just finished singing and the stage had gone dark again, the Shed also dark and empty and quiet. It was the lone light in the back corner that suddenly flickered three times and then stayed, prompting Lars to turn his head, and there she was, the silhouette of her figure pointed in the direction of the lawn, her silver hair shining under that solitary beam.

It appeared she was wearing only a heavy sweater, difficult to tell the exact color from his distance but its surface seemed soft, like cashmere. Standing, Lars was just beginning to tiptoe closer when music over the P.A. momentarily broke his focus. The volume was very low, but he could clearly make out the sound of a piano repeatedly playing the ascending figure from the movement

Vigeland

of a concerto he had once heard in this very place. Saint-Saens? He wondered if she could hear it, too, but the rain was coming down harder and soon the sound of that rain hitting the roof of the Shed and the ground beyond it was dominant.

Lars had reached the last row of the seats, from which place he had a very clear view of her back. Except for her breathing, she was motionless, and though he could not see her face he had the sense that she was staring at something out in the wide wet gloom…or perhaps it was elsewhere, far away. He tried to hold his breath as he took a step closer, but then he froze as she reached down to the hem of her sweater, which she pulled up and over her head and then dropped. She raised her arms and extended them forward, as if in a blessing motion. She held that pose for several minutes. Then, reaching down again, she picked up the sweater in her right hand.

A Symphony for Shelbie

Lars had moved closer, so when she tossed the sweater in the air it was an easy catch for him — or so he expected, but when he grabbed it, there was nothing to feel, no weight, no heft, just the shape of a sweater. And then it was gone and so, too, was his last ghost, across the lawn, through the rain, running.

Vigeland

III: *THIS MUSIC CREPT BY ME*

Long after Shelbie Murphy's death, I was still trying to understand something Dr. Klement said could not be explained. We were walking near the buildings of Harvard Medical School, where she'd worked more than a decade earlier, when she first came to Boston. She could of course explicate what had happened…"but no one knows," she told me after a brunch at the diner where we'd first met, "except maybe God," and this from someone who never went to church, except on the occasion for a memorial service when she'd lost one of her patients.

It was summer again in the city that used to be called the Athens of America, the civic pride of which now seemed in keeping with my own authorial hubris. What a sadly self-centered ambition in contrast to the daily struggle of Giannoula's young cancer patients simply to find themselves alive the next morning, something that neither Irina's math could model nor my musical memories could mime.

The BSO was going to present Mahler's Eighth, the so-called *Symphony of a Thousand*, at Tanglewood. Andris Nelsons would be conducting. Singing in the chorus would be Irina, who this year had been the soloist in an April concert of a local regional orchestra. We'd been to a couple of BSO concerts at Symphony Hall, after which over coffee we picked up the conversation about music and medicine we'd begun two years earlier, when we'd met that summer afternoon in the Berkshires. She continued to sign her emails, "sqrt(-1)"—the

Vigeland

square root of minus one—a mathematical impossibility and, for me, a kind of shorthand for the very mystery that she had addressed in a comparison of platelet activation in wounds and tumors (the start of the process is remarkably similar, but with tumors it doesn't stop).

Lee Elman, the friend with whom I was speaking the day I first met Irina—and the subject of a short book I was working on then and that had since been published—had recently invited me to stay overnight at his estate if I were planning to be at Tanglewood's festival within a festival, a week-long omnibus of new music. With thanks, I told him I hoped instead to hear the rehearsals for Mahler, and could I stay a couple of nights then?

"Yes, of course," came the immediate response.

The day before I drove over, I called someone I knew in the orchestra's press office to secure permission to attend the rehearsals—there were several, Irina had written me—something I'd done often when I was working on my second book years earlier. "You'd better send a written request," I was told. I went ahead and did so, and when I didn't hear anything back I assumed all was fine.

That turned out to be a mistake, though a providential one. When I arrived at Tanglewood I was told that the Shed was closed to visitors during the rehearsal. After failing to plead my case, I took a seat on one of the outside benches and listened to maybe five minutes of the music before leaving for Elman's and a quick dinner at a small restaurant nearby where I've stopped many times on my way back from New York. That night I attended a Schubert recital and then the next morning awoke with the realization that the entire day was free—I had originally planned to be at two

Vigeland

more Mahler rehearsals—and so, following breakfast in town and feeling almost as if what I was
about to do was preordained in the genetic mate-
rial of my life, I decided to look for the path to the
river I had taken almost three years earlier, shortly
after the Saint Saens rehearsal with the French pianist.

Though a warm day had been predicted, it
was cloudy and a little chilly that morning, so over
my tee shirt I wore a fleece vest that I soon took
off—to my regret, since the mosquitoes were feast-
ing. From Lee's house I headed downhill in a west-
erly direction, past tidy rows of grape vines that
ended with woods of second or third growth. I
took a right turn there and followed one of the
many trails on which he and his friends often rode
on horseback. Eventually, I came into a large clearing, a meadow that had not been mowed and from
which there seemed no exit. On its far side, I cut

through some bushes and found myself on a dirt road that I immediately recognized as the one I had discovered on my original hike, back on the day I'd first looked for that swimming spot and then, afterwards, driven into Aston Magna and met Lee.

It was an easy walk along this road to the river, which I reached in another ten or 15 minutes, ending on a bank that the town kept mowed, near the bottom of another horse path that I realized was the one I should have taken because it came directly from Lee's vineyard. I would return that way, but first I walked out onto a loosely formed dam of rocks and boulders that had been con-structed as a barrier for a pool to form behind it, deep enough for swimming. I found a place on the rocks that was dry, with the river running triplet-like on either side, and took a seat.

Vigeland

Though I would have been too young to re-member, I wondered if I had been taken swim-ming in this same river when I was an infant. After the war, when my father returned from Europe, coming back to the Berkshires would have been impractical. He and my mother had been married before he went overseas, and now they wanted to start a family. He soon found a position at a church in Englewood, New Jersey, where I was born and where we lived until moving to Buffalo in 1950.

From stories I remembered their sharing, usually when we were looking at old photographs, I knew that we often came back to this area that had been such an important part of my father's early adulthood. Usually we stayed in a cabin atop Mount Everett in the tiny hamlet of Mount Wash-ington—I'd never been able to make sense of the two names—often sharing space with the family of my father's only sibling, a younger brother who had been a P.O.W. One of their Berkshires friends had turned an old inn into a place he called the Folly—it had long since again become an inn—but I didn't think we'd ever stayed there. Instead, it was the locale of many parties, with a pond-size pool in back on which floated an armada of miniature boats, a picture window in the dining room that looked out on a well-taken care of golf tee, replete with yardage sign, ball washer, and bench, that went nowhere (though years later I learned there had once been a short golf course that wound its way around the property), and a toy train that ran on tracks from the kitchen to the bar in the dining room, on which someone's sandwich might be delivered via one of the cars.

Ever afterwards on summer vacation trips, we would detour through the Berkshires, however far removed they may have been from our actual destination (the Adirondacks; Vermont; Maine).

Vigeland

And always, right up to that summer when we lived in the home of that old girlfriend of my father's, we'd be led on what I think of now as field trips to all of my father's former haunts— the estate of an elderly dowager to whom he'd given piano lessons, an antiques store whose proprietor played a legendary though unexplained role in my father's memory, a sign painter whose Great Barrington shop was a favorite place to hangout, and of course Aston Magna—this was before Elman bought it—where, I would discover in my dad's diaries that I read after his death, he sometimes dined with Albert Spalding and his wife before playing four-handed piano music with the great musician. Again and again there would be this sequence of person-place-memory, person-place-memory.

Like father, like son.

*

A Symphony for Shelbie

Mesmerized by the sound of the running water, I was startled to attention by a voice behind me.

"Hey!"

I looked up.

Standing there, on another boulder, was a man who looked about my age.

"Hello," I said, stretching out my hand to meet his. "I'm...," I started to say, but he interrupted me.

"I know your name," he said.

"But who are you?" I asked.

"I am Lars."

"Take a seat," I said, trembling, my voice seeming to pulsate with the rhythm of the running water. Was it my imagination, or did Lars look at me with a hint of compassion?

"I think when I left you in the Shed late that September night, it had been raining," I said.

"Correct."

Vigeland

"There was a woman wearing a sweater, and after she threw it at you, she started running across the Tanglewood lawn."

"Correct."

"I always wondered—did you ever see her again?"

"You're asking me? I should be asking you!"

"It was...is...complicated."

"And?"

"And so, I dropped it. You. Left you...it...hanging."

"Thanks a lot."

"I had other, more pressing issues."

"Such as?"

"Well, to begin with, I was out here one day, shortly after I'd started to write about your night at Tanglewood, and I met someone who owned a house—an estate—I hadn't been to in years, a

A Symphony for Shelbie

place that had played an important role in my father's life when he was a young man."

By now, Lars had taken a seat on a nearby boulder. I noticed he was barefoot, and he was pulling at the pants legs of his jeans as he let his toes touch the water, at which he was staring. He did not respond to what I had last said. Should I go on, I wondered. What was prompting my sudden reticence?

"As a boy," I said, "I used to perform on the trumpet sometimes, with my father accompanying on the organ. Usually it was something from the standard trumpet repertory—Purcell, Bach, or a contemporary work by Alan Hovhaness—though once my dad wrote something for me to play."

Was Lars even listening?

"My performances with my father were always at the church where he was the organist. Playing, I'd be standing in the back of the choir loft, and when we were done I'd sit by my father on the organ bench during the rest of the service. From that perch I could see the whole congregation, though my focus was invariably on the senior pastor—at our church we referred to him as a minister—an older man with thinning, gray hair and glasses, over whose white shirt and suit he wore a black robe."

Still no response, but my doppelganger was clearly paying attention.

"This was an era, in the decades immediately following the Second World War, when among the elite of what I later came to understand was the orthodoxy of liberal Protestantism, certain men of the cloth, as they were also called, were renowned for the inspiration of their preaching. The minister at my father's church was among these men—they were, back then, all men—whose sermons powerfully addressed questions of contemporary meaning in the face of the recent war's wholesale slaughter of many millions. The actual number of casualties, of course, was so obscenely large as to defy a specific count, so that even the number of people who had perished in the Holocaust was rounded off, a fact that to me had the consequence of making the reality it represented even more unfathomable.

"Listening from up high at the far end of the church, I was so taken by one of the minister's sermons that I later took to quoting something from it, even as he himself was quoting someone else. The occasion for this particular sermon has been lost on me, though I am guessing it may have had to do with an anniversary of some sort relative to the Peace Bridge that connected the city of Buffalo, across the Niagara River, with Canada. In any event, the sermon ended—as did the minister's

Vigeland

quotation from a book by *Our Town* playwright Thornton Wilder—with the following sentence: 'There is a land of the living and land of the dead, and the bridge is love, the only survival, the only meaning.'"

Lars was still silent.

"I was just now thinking about a story that starts with some music at Tanglewood," I said. "Or I guess it actually begins here, the actual story I mean, and then it continues in Boston, though the part I was just thinking about now happened in New Hampshire after I'd been visiting my sister in Maine…"

"I know," Lars interrupted me, as if he were some kind of a mind-reader.

I'd taken my running shoes and socks off and, like Lars, let my feet dangle in the water, rhythmic in its flow over the rocks. I wondered how long—how much water—must pass before an incremental change in the size of a rock could be measured.

One hundred years? A thousand?

"The story's key is not strands but threads," I said, "which when Dr. Klement talks about cancer is reduced to a single word: systemic. It is this insight that not only defines her work but also, for me, brings together the music in the Tanglewood Shed, the research in Giannoula's former lab, baseball at Fenway Park, the throngs of people by the harbor, Harvard Yard, my Revere memories, Bobby Joe Leaster...they are all of a piece, the Gordian knot of my experience, if you will." And, I wanted to add, it was how they were threaded, not just what, that insofar as I understood the intersection of genetics and environment prompted or created...a feeling, a growth, a realization...the prospect of a kind of resilience, a going forward, like

Vigeland

the notes in a great piece of music leading the listener if not to redemption than to grace.

Lars looked a bit puzzled. "Why are you telling me this?" he asked. Instead of answering him directly, I continued on a different but related tack.

"The day after a wrenching phone conversation with an English woman, married to an American man, whose eight-year-old daughter had a glioblastoma—a brain tumor—with very poor prognosis, my wife woke me with the news that our youngest had gone into labor. We spent the rest of the day and the entire following night at the hospital, where at one point there was an emergency when the baby's heartbeat plummeted, prebirth. All eventually turned out well, and we are now grandparents for the second time. The next day, a longtime old golf friend, since relocated to Vermont, died at fifty-four of a drug overdose, leaving his divorced wife and two teenaged children. After a late lunch, I headed up to see baby and new parents with a detour first to a favorite swimming spot, where on a very hot late afternoon I encountered fifty or sixty skinny dippers of both genders, many ages, and widely varied body shapes, and when I arrived home I opened a package from my brother that contained a new CD of piano music he had composed, performed by a Chinese-born virtuoso."

From the look on his face, Lars seemed off somewhere else.

Just then, from a direction far beyond the river and adjacent woods, I heard three retorts or thunderclaps. Then, nothing.

"Believe what I have run into again," I continued, "is the same thing, obstacle, I used to avoid back when, always under the guise of not wishing to hurt anyone, whereas the person I have really

Vigeland

been protecting is myself, in my life, in my writing, and at what cost, though cost is a different story. That leaves the furtive obstacle, how to share as I would wish to share with others the truth about myself, not because any reader may wish to know but because a reader might in my sharing sense something about theirs, a secret connection if you will, a liberation, which reminds me of famous Hemingway dictum: you can leave out anything if you know you are leaving it out. So, I can put in the wind in those tall trees on the enormous lawn by the Tanglewood Shed, but leave out knowing I am leaving out who heard that wind with 'you,' who looked across that lawn with 'you,' who took...my hand in the darkness backstage when...I proffered it as in a gesture of safety, as in don't slip here by the stage docking, but the gesture may have been much more than that, at once spontane-ous and premeditated subconsciously.

A Symphony for Shelbie

"An older English professor friend once re-minded me in a telephone conversation that hap-pened to be about a Mississippi civil rights story I was working on, which I thought might become a book, that what I was writing was not a document but...a book; big difference, he didn't need to add, I could already hear it in the admonition of his voice.

"No doubt this even traces back to my youthful reticence, but that, too, is another story, or a detail I am leaving out because I just realized I know I am leaving it out, the loss of a love I car-ried with me to college, soon encumbered further by the loss that my father's demise came to repre-sent, and then I met my future wife, and again what I hear in what I am saying is a longing that no one can or ever will answer, because that kind of burden cannot fairly be placed on someone else."

Vigeland

"Insofar as I grasp it," Lars finally replied, "my motive has always been for the same reason that drove me even as a boy to find my version of the music of the spheres. I am happy now to be still, so to speak, and all this now is still crossed always with music, what I had, what I knew, and, over time, have put into a different context—forgive me that last word—so that when I am back again in my memory behind that stage curtain, 'you' are also simultaneously on the marrow floor in Boston...transcendence indeed, or grace by another name.

"One day out of the blue as I meditated upon awakening, I had something of an epiphany over a search, beginning with the trumpeters and trumpet makers I have known and worked with and going backwards to my own playing and then further back to some of the greats from the past and then further still, working in among other things everyone from Leroy Anderson and his *Bugler's Holiday* to Haydn to taps to the concept of a clarion call to the mathematical concept of the archangel's horn. I already knew the musical part of this and in fact had written much of in different framework.

"Suppose that spring at last had come to the Berkshires, but since in May the late afternoons could be chilly, along with the food and wine I'd bought at Guido's I packed a blanket and extra sweater with my sleeping bag. In case the repo man had any new ideas, I locked the front door of my cottage and walked to my car. A slight breeze had come up and I could hear the lake lapping against the pilings that held up my dock. I'd put it in early that year after the mild winter we'd had, though the water was still too cold to swim in. None of my summer neighbors had moved in yet, but I could see from the open windows in his

Vigeland

house that Rothman was home. I needed to get going on his book. Not just now."

"Wow," I said to Lars. "Where'd you come up with that one?"

But of course I knew the answer.

"It was a very rainy morning," I continued, returning finally to the New Hampshire story I had been about to tell him earlier. "The summer season not yet underway, his shop in fact just opened. I was not sure if I should intrude, though the day before I already in a sense had, pausing on my way to Maine to see his daughter, whom I met at a Starbucks at a Barnes & Noble near Lowell, and she told me about her parents going to New Hampshire every summer and I asked might I stop and meet them and she had said, 'yes, of course.'

"But then, the next day as I headed home, I was uncertain, thought maybe I would just find the place and see it, which I did after a little de-touring, and it was much smaller than I had ex-pected, and next to a clam shack. In the rain it was hard to take a good photo from my car in the small lot across the road, so I walked over to look in the window and when I did there was no one inside except him, and when he looked up and saw me I realized I had to come in, which I did and he—in tee shirt and Bermuda shorts—took his place be-hind the counter and I said hello, are you Mr. Patenaude, and he looked startled, that I knew who he was, and he said yes. And as I explained who I was, as soon as I said her name...Shelbie... he stepped away and walked to the back of the small store, to compose himself.

"When he returned, this big, strong, 70year-old grandfather, once a construction worker, put his hand out, and said, 'My wife will be so sorry she is not here, she has arthritis that was really

Vigeland

bothering her so she is back at our cottage. I am so glad to meet you. Would you like some candy, some fudge, whatever you'd like.'

"When I went to pay, he told me my money was not good in this store. He showed me photos on the wall of the candy making, and there were some plastic bracelets in a trinket counter.

"'Shelbie made them' he said.

"This time I needed a moment to get hold of myself.

"I chose one of the bracelets for my older granddaughter whom I was going to be visiting the next weekend. Again, he would not let me pay. Then he packed a box of fudge for me to take home for my wife. We shook hands, and I walked in the rain back to my car."

"Lars?"

I looked around.

A Symphony for Shelbie

All I saw was were trees on the banks of the river and the flowing water, the sky, the sunlight. And in my mind a face.

All I heard was the water gurgling through the rocks, a chorus of many voices...Ishmael... Miss Snapworth...Francois...Gabriel...Ava...Irina... Lee...Bonnie...the promptings in my heart that took me to all those other places only to find, finally, the ghosts of the past—mine; anyone's— transmuted in the poignantly transient present by the living, breathing, triumphant spirit of a brave, beautiful, extraordinary young woman whom I never met—by the time I asked, I was told it was too late—yet felt, like everyone in her wide, grateful, awestruck circle, I loved.

Vigeland

IV: *THE DOVE*

"Shelbie loved music, nature, singing, cars, animals, her family and friends, her cat Violet and dog Murray," her mother Jackie told me when I first met her in February, two months after Shelbie's death. "She loved to attend concerts, shopping at the mall, she loved crafts and fairs. She loved to read, sketch, painting her nails and nail art, going to the movies. She had a huge admiration for my father. She loved him with all her heart."

Jackie and I spoke in the basement apartment of the large house she shared with her parents and one of her sisters and that sister's adult son—Shelbie's adult cousin, who had cerebral palsy. Later, she continued telling me about Shelbie's life via email.

"Shelbie was born on May 14, 1997 at 10:55 a.m. at Lowell General Hospital in Lowell, Massachusetts. My mother, her father, and one of my sisters were all there to welcome her into the world. She was a very independent child. She would always seem to entertain herself. She had a love for animals and when she was small she wanted to become a veterinarian one day. She loved anything to do with art and would often draw.

"At the age of seven she was diagnosed with A.D.D., which made it very hard for her to focus. Once we got her the proper help and medication she did very well dealing with it. Although she was a very shy girl she would always try to get involved with friends and anything related to school. She went to the Christa McAuliffe School for elementary and the Robinson Middle School, both in Lowell. Despite her A.D.D. and anxiety she

Vigeland

always managed to keep up with her schooling and made the honor roll several times.

"Her father and I divorced when she was seven and she lived with me full time. She would see her dad two days a week and every other weekend.

"Shelbie had such a love for life. She loved to sing. She started singing when she was two years old and she knew many artists, young and old. She loved all kinds of music, but she was not into musicals. She loved cars, and when she was little she would play for hours with match box cars. But far from being a tomboy, she always had some kind of fashion sense and she loved anything vintage. I used to call her my 'old soul.'

"My daughter relapsed after being in remission for nineteen months. With our heads held down and lost for words my daughter wiped my tears and said, 'Mama it will be all right.' I was so

A Symphony for Shelbie

angry and till this day I still am. I may not show it but I am completely broken on the inside. My daughter went through so much in the last three years. She took my breath away. She was a true fighter and as hard as the last weeks were for her she still shined on.

"Cancer is a nightmare. Cancer if you allow it will suck the life right out of you. Cancer robbed my child of having a normal life. My sad days were days when I saw her beg for this to end, to see her sob because she wanted to feel 'NORMAL.' The last year for me was more mentally trying than physical.

"I want to thank Shelbie's team of doctors, nurses, therapists, social workers and parent liaisons for all their support and love for my daughter. I also want to thank my family, for without them I would not be who I am today. And to all of my friends for their continued prayers and love for

Vigeland

my Shelbie. And most of all I would like to thank my beautiful daughter for teaching me what true strength is all about, for showing me what true love is between a mother and her child.

"At the age of 13, when she was diagnosed with Stage Four Ewing's Sarcoma, she had to leave school for a year and a half while she was in treatment. She went back to school for eighth grade, part time, and tutored at home the other days. It was very hard for her. She was bald and very insecure. She started high school that fall and attended Greater Lowell Technical High school in Tyngsboro, Massachusetts. She decided to go into painting and interior design as her career choice. She then started to blossom. She made several friends. She loved her shop and she loved her teachers as well as they loved her. She had so much potential and her teachers made sure she was recognized for it.

A Symphony for Shelbie

"Her designs and sketches are just phenomenal. She did all this while still being under treatment at Tufts Floating Hospital. She would go into clinic every three weeks for an antibody treatment. When she fell out of remission, her protocol changed and radiation was also introduced. She went into Boston everyday for four weeks and never complained.

"She would always say, 'I want to talk to you, but not about cancer.' She never let cancer define her. Another of her favorite quotes was, 'A trying time is no time to quit trying.' She believed in that and it helped her get through.

"During the final very hard year Shelbie was recognized for many things. She had a photo shoot with Dr. Klement and me for an article about targeted therapy. She also advocated for Childhood Cancer Awareness and spoke with Beecher Grogan, founder of Lucy's Love Bus.

Vigeland

"Shelbie also received many outstanding achievement awards at school. She was featured in the local Lowell newspaper twice and in *Boston Magazine* for a story on the Prom to Remember. She was also on the local television news, speaking about that event."

A Symphony for Shelbie

A week before Christmas, Dr. Klement had advised the family that Shelbie had little time left. The family's Christmas observance was moved up four days to December twenty-first. One by one the various aunts and uncles and Shelbie's maternal grandparents came into her room to say goodbye. Before she lost consciousness, Shelbie said she wished to be taken back to Floating Hospital to her other "family." Her father Tom called a friend in the fire department who managed to procure an ambulance, even though the hospice nurse advised moving her from Lowell. Accompanied by her mother and an aunt, Shelbie made it in the ambulance to Boston early that evening.

The city was quiet, the hospital, too, the hallways deserted, most of the other young patients asleep. Beginning what they thought would be an all-night vigil, the group gathered in her room, her father and mother and Dr. Klement by her bedside.

Vigeland

"I'll be right back," Jackie said a few minutes before midnight as she kissed her daughter's forehead before stepping out into the hallway to gather herself again, to breathe.

"I never thought it was going to happen right then," Jackie would tell me later. "When I came back…she was gone."

Jackie spent several minutes alone in the room with her only daughter's body, beginning a communication with the evanescence of her memory that would take Jackie through the funeral service, burial in what was to have been a plot for Shelbie's maternal grandparents, a long winter of grieving, and planning for the summer placement on Shelbie's burial place of a stone engraved with the image of a dove.

The last time I saw Jackie, she loaned me two copies of old editions of the Lowell newspaper, *The*

Sun. The first, from about a year and a half before Shelbie died, was on page one and focused on a "makeover" of her bedroom that was paid for with foundation help and volunteer labor. The second, which ran when Shelbie had only a few months to live, was a fundraising appeal for expenses of her care not covered by insurance.

Throughout this period and in the time since, a steady stream of Facebook posts had appeared on both Jackie's and Shelbie's pages, with Shelbie's, subsequently entitled Shelbie R.I.P., kept going by Jackie. The posts take us back through Shelbie's life, from a photo of her in kindergarten to many during her various stages of treatment to one of her seated in a wheelchair at high school, in front of a row of lockers and surrounded by classmates. With her left hand she makes a V for victory, as do all her friends. Some of the posts on Jackie's page feature other children with cancer, including an obituary of a young woman whom I recognized, without having known the name, as the patient Giannoula had told me about the evening we'd gone back to the hospital so she could retrieve something she'd left on the marrow floor.

Before Shelbie died, Jackie told me, Shelbie had been reading a novel as part of the schoolwork she did when she could no longer attend school and so a tutor came to her home. The novel was Salinger's *Catcher in the Rye*, and Shelbie had been so engaged reading it that she often did so out loud, to Jackie, and then they would discuss what she'd just read. She would also talk about each chapter of the iconic book with her tutor, until one day she could neither hold the book nor concentrate while someone read to her. She had just reached Chapter 14 when she could not go on.

"Such pain, such grace," Jackie said. "When she knew she was dying, she comforted me.

A Symphony for Shelbie

"We will never know why," she continued, echoing the very thing Giannoula would say. "You need to start forgetting why or it will make yourself sick. You have to accept that there is no answer, that the body will do what it wants to do.

"It's going to be okay, Mom," Jackie told me she said. *"It's time for you now, Mom.*

"She meant that I would no longer need to devote myself to her care. I cried on her lap and held her hand.

"I know you're sad, Mom. I will help you. It is time for you to live."

Vigeland

Acknowledgments

Many people helped to make this book become a reality, none more so than Dr. Klement and Shelbie's mother, JackieAnn Murphy. My thanks to them are long and deep. As the book chronicles, I met Jackie though Giannoula, just as I met Giannoula through Irina Kareva, who had entered my life by chance on a summer's day at the summer home of my friend Lee Elman. Special thanks to both of them for beginning what became an ever-widening circle of friendship and acquaintance, which in turn crossed with others, going back to my first childhood visit to Symphony Hall and following forward to my fictionalized Tanglewood tale. To plot or delineate each contact or connection that brought me, finally, to the same river spot I was looking for at the beginning would be to

A Symphony for Shelbie

write the book again. Instead, permit me a discursive gratitude, incorporating person by person the multi-layered strands of this book's DNA.

First, however, let me clarify that except in my "auto-fiction" encounters with ghosts and one or two people for whose privacy I invented an identity, all other names are real. That said, the imagined encounter between Nathaniel Hawthorne and Herman Melville is based, word for word, on a few quotations I took from a Tanglewood diary Hawthorne kept (available in several reprints) and part of a chapter in the great book Melville dedicated to his Berkshires neighbor, with whom he spent many hours in conversation as *Moby Dick* neared its conclusion.

To continue, then, at Tanglewood, I am grateful to Bruce Peeples, who oversees the beautiful grounds of this great institution—which, since Lars encountered his ghosts, has expanded

Vigeland

its campus with the Tanglewood Learning Institute, newly built on or very near the site of the former apple orchard that Lars references.

Tanglewood, of course, means the Boston Symphony Orchestra, to which I owe lifelong thanks for both music and friendship. In the case of this book, I am especially indebted to Bernadette Horgan, the orchestra's director of public relations, and until recently her associate, Taryn Lott, and assistant, Sam Brewer.

I checked my Tanglewood history in Jeremy Yudkin's *The Lenox School of Jazz, Hawthorne's Lenox* by Cornelia Brooke Gilder with Julian Conklin Peters, and *Music Under the Moon* by John G. W. Mahanna.

On many trips to Boston, my usual destination was the lab that Giannoula oversaw at that time at Tufts Medical Center. In addition to Abdo Abou-Slaybi and Irina, I am indebted there to

A Symphony for Shelbie

Nandita Bhattacharia, Jenn Dagesse, Olga Dashevsky, Oliver Dodd, Laura Flynn, Allison Jenks, Mingying Liao, Nelson Moreira, Edward Rietman, and Tine Roffidal. Despite my lack of formal scientific training, I was welcomed on my visits, during which I often felt I was going back to school.

Early on in my research and reporting, I had the great good fortune of repeated conversation with the esteemed editor-in-chief emeritus of *The Atlantic*, William Whitworth. Though any errors or misunderstandings in this book are mine, his kindness, probing questions, and wise advice meant much to me. I am grateful as well to the late Richard Todd; Dean Robinson at *The New York Times Magazine*; Christopher Cox, at the time the editor-in-chief of *Harper's Magazine*; Hendrick Hertzberg at the *New Yorker*; Dr. Jerome Groopman; David Tripp, now retired from Perseus Books; Wayne Kabak; and Bob Bender at Simon & Schuster.

Vigeland

To Peter and Laura Ickes, my thanks for bed and board; to Bill and Vicki Hart, thank you for your support; for Berkshires hospitality, thank you Judy Ney; thanks to Denis Laflamme for listening and to the entire D'Ambrosio family for welcoming me into their home; and thanks to physical therapist John Prinzivalli and Dr. Jeffrey L. Kaufman, both of whom listened repeatedly and with encouragement to anecdotes that became part of this book.

Finally, my wife Bonnie, all three of my adult children—Christian, Anna, and Maren — and my extended family—brother Nils, sister Astrid, sister-in-law Maddy and daughter-in-law Lauren, and Peter Balov and Emrys Bond—offered encouragement, and Anna made numerous critical suggestions after repeated readings. My college classmate and dear friend Stuart Schoffman was always "there" when I needed him, even though he lives in Israel, thousands of miles from my home. And my literary agent Christopher Vyce was ever present with his passion, expertise, empathy, and friendship.

Vigeland

Made in the USA
Middletown, DE
31 January 2020